Grade 6

W9-AQJ-440

Practice Book
O

Macmillan
McGraw-Hill

The McGraw·Hill Companies

Macmillan
McGraw-Hill

Published by Macmillan/McGraw-Hill, of McGraw-Hill Education, a division of The McGraw-Hill Companies, Inc., Two Penn Plaza, New York, New York 10121.

Copyright © by Macmillan/McGraw-Hill. All rights reserved. No part of this publication may be reproduced or distributed in any form or by any means, or stored in a database or retrieval system, without the prior written consent of The McGraw-Hill Companies, Inc., including, but not limited to, network storage or transmission, or broadcast for distance learning.

Printed in the United States of America

9 10 079 09 08

Contents

© Macmillan/McGraw-Hill

Unit 2 • Saving the Day

© Macmillan/McGraw-Hill

Unit 3 • Great Ideas

© Macmillan/McGraw-Hill

Unit 4 • Achievements

© Macmillan/McGraw-Hill

Unit 5 • Turning Points

© Macmillan/McGraw-Hill

Unit 6 • Yesterday, Today, and Tomorrow

© Macmillan/McGraw-Hill

Name _____

Use the vocabulary words below to complete the sentences.

intersection	engulf	abruptly	conscious
anxiety	cascade	procedure	souvenir

1. Marian often had the best ideas, but her _____ about public speaking kept her from running for class president.

2. I would have liked to take a _____ from the archaeological site, but it was strictly forbidden.

3. Though the task was not difficult, I had to be careful to follow the
   _____ exactly.

4. We were startled when the author _____ closed her book and left.

5. The actor was extremely well trained—always _____ of the audience's reaction to his performance.

6. The papers fell in a _____ from the top of the shelf.

7. I was taught to look both ways when crossing an _____.

8. The huge wave was about to _____ the tiny islands in the sea.

Choose two of the vocabulary words in the box above and write a sentence for each.

9. _____

   _____

10. _____

    _____

    _____

© Macmillan/McGraw-Hill

Read the passage and answer the questions.

It was dark when I woke up. I was so cold. At first, I didn't know where I was. I started to panic. I couldn't move my arms or legs. What was happening to me? Then I remembered. I had been skiing. I had heard a really loud noise, like a freight train. When I had looked behind me, all I had seen was a wall of snow coming my way—fast!

"I must be buried in that snow," I said to myself. Talk about panic! Now I had a good reason. To make myself feel better, I thought about all the TV shows I had watched about people being rescued. I drifted in and out of consciousness.

Meanwhile, I learned later, the rescue teams were gathering, just like on TV! Several skiers were missing after the avalanche. Luckily, I had been skiing on a marked path. The rescue teams would know where to look for me. After what seemed like forever, I heard voices. I tried to scream, but the snow covering me blocked any noise. At last, I felt something touch my legs. A dog was digging me out. I had been rescued!

1. What do you know about the narrator? _____

_____

_____

2. Where is the story set?

_____

3. How does the setting affect the story?

_____

_____

_____

4. What is the main conflict in the story?

_____

_____

© Macmillan/McGraw-Hill

At Home: Tell a story about a rescue. Discuss the conflict and how the setting and characters affect the plot.

Name _____

As you read *The Summer of the Swans,* fill in the Story Map.

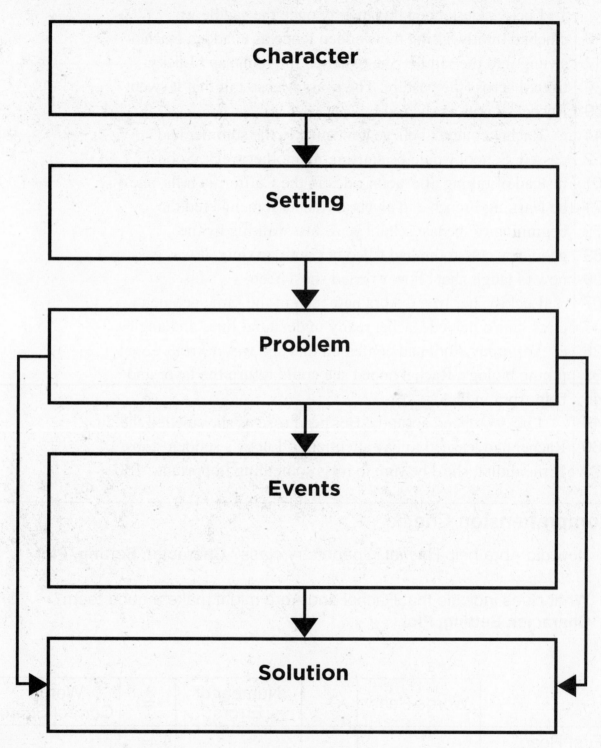

How does the information you wrote in this Story Map help you monitor comprehension of *The Summer of the Swans*?

At Home: Have the student use the map to retell the story.

The Summer of the Swans
Grade 6/Unit I

3

© Macmillan/McGraw-Hill

As I read, I will pay attention to pauses and stops.

	Lucky sidestepped impatiently once the saddle was
7	cinched tightly. Using the wooden fence as a ladder, Rachel
17	swung into the saddle. She twitched the reins, and Lucky
27	trotted across the pasture. The grass was so tall that it swept
39	Rachel's boots as she rode.
44	Rachel couldn't believe how quickly the summer had
52	passed. School would be starting in another week. Soon,
61	instead of taking afternoon rides in the California hills, she'd
71	be learning French and algebra. Rachel remembered the
79	beginning of the last school year. Just walking by the
89	geometry classroom had filled her with **anxiety.** It was easy
99	now to laugh about how worried she'd been.
107	Luckily, her friend Abra had been in the same geometry
117	class. She'd helped Rachel really understand lines and angles.
126	Yesterday Abra had confessed that she was nervous about
135	taking biology. Rachel hoped she could return the favor and
145	help Abra in biology.
149	Lucky stopped abruptly. Her head rose as she smelled the air.
160	Rachel had learned to pay attention to Lucky's sudden stops.
170	If she didn't, she'd be sure to miss something important. 180

Comprehension Check

1. How did Abra help Rachel in geometry class? **Character, Setting, Plot**

2. What clues indicate that Rachel and Abra might make a good team?
   Character, Setting, Plot

	Words Read	–	Number of Errors	=	Words Correct Score
First Read		–		=	
Second Read		–		=	

© Macmillan/McGraw-Hill

At Home: Help the student read the passage, paying attention to the goal at the top of the page.

Name _____

A **photo caption** explains the situation in which the photograph was taken. Captions give information about the people or events shown in the photo. They may answer some of the questions readers want to know, such as *who, what, when, where, why,* and *how.*

Look at the illustration and read the caption. Then answer the questions.

Sparky Rescued! Monday, February 14, Philadelphia, PA—Firefighter Cathy Lewis carries Sparky, a ten-year-old beagle, from his burning home. The beagle was unconscious when firefighter Lewis pulled him out of the fire. Sparky is being treated in an animal clinic. Photo by Ninti Alfred.

1. What is the title of the caption? _____

2. How does the caption title hint at the photo's content? _____
_____

3. What do you learn from the dateline? _____
_____

4. Who took the photograph? _____

5. Summarize the information in the photo by answering these questions.

   Who is in the picture?

   _____

   _____

   Why is this picture in the paper?

   _____

© Macmillan/McGraw-Hill

At Home: Together, find another photo or illustration and make up your own caption for it.

Multiple-meaning words have more than one definition. When you come across a multiple-meaning word, you need to determine which meaning is being used by looking at its context. These words will have various entries in the dictionary.

Consider the multiple meanings of the word *conscious.*

> **conscious** (kon shəs) *adj.*
> 1. having an awareness of one's self and one's surroundings; *The patient remained conscious after her surgery.*
> 2. fully aware of something; *I was not conscious that time was passing quickly.*
> 3. intentionally meant: *Marianne made a conscious effort not to tease her little brother.*

Each word below has more than one meaning. Use a dictionary to identify two different meanings for each word. Write two sentences—one for each meaning of the word.

1. kind

  a. _____

  b. _____

2. produce

  a. _____

  b. _____

3. proceeds

  a. _____

  b. _____

4. park

  a. _____

  b. _____

At Home: Together, provide multiple meanings for the word *catch.* Use each one in a sentence.

© Macmillan/McGraw-Hill

Short vowel sounds are often spelled using just the vowel itself. For example, the letter *u* stands for the /u/ sound in *bug, cut,* and *nun.* The letter *i* stands for the /i/ sound in *big, kick,* and *lid.* Sometimes short vowel sounds have different spellings. For example, the /u/ sound is spelled by the *ou* in *trouble* and the *o* in *shove.* The short /e/ sound can be spelled by the *ea* in *thread.*

Read the word in the left column. Then circle the words on the right that make the same short vowel sound using a different spelling.

rug   bone   done   through   shove   over   double   money   though

din   rhythm   encyclopedia   pretty   very   myth   women

let   fiend   friend   said   laid   haystack   says   thread   head

Choose five of the words above that have the short vowel sound in them. Write a sentence for each word you chose. Underline the word you chose in each sentence.

1. _____

_____

2. _____

_____

3. _____

_____

4. _____

_____

5. _____

_____

© Macmillan/McGraw-Hill

At Home: Play word games, listing as many words as you can with short vowel sounds. List basic spellings in one column and variant spellings in another.

Use the clues to complete the crossword.

remote   withstood   venomous   vegetation
undergrowth   interpreter   escort   foretold

Across

4. low vegetation on the floor of a forest
5. a person who accompanies another to give protection
7. secluded
8. resisted the effect of

Down

1. poisonous
2. plants
3. person who translates
6. predicted

© Macmillan/McGraw-Hill

Read the passage. Then answer the questions.

"How does a whole city get lost?" Todd asked his mother.

"It isn't actually lost," she explained. "It's more like people forgot it was there."

Todd was very excited. He and his mother were on their way to visit Machu Picchu. It was the first time Todd and his mother would be going to Peru.

The tour guide explained that Machu Picchu, or at least what was left of it, was discovered by a man named Hiram Bingham. Todd listened intently as the tour guide described the dangers Bingham and his crew faced while trying to reach the city—a city they were not sure even existed!

"At least we don't have to cut our way through the forest to get there," Todd said. His mother agreed.

When the tour guide finished, both Todd and his mother settled into their train seats to take in the view of the rain forest.

Todd tried to imagine the way Bingham had felt as he climbed the mountain. Todd could hardly wait to see the actual city. It was going to be one of the best times of his life, he was sure. When he finally arrived, he was not disappointed.

1. What happens in the story? _____

_____

2. Who is the main character of the story? _____

3. Where is the story set? _____

_____

4. How does Todd feel about seeing Machu Picchu? _____

_____

5. What does Todd learn on the way? _____

_____

© Macmillan/McGraw-Hill

At Home: Together, work to illustrate the passage above.
Include details of the setting.

Name _____

As you read *Lost City,* **fill in the Character, Setting, Plot Chart.**

Character	Setting	Plot

How does the information you wrote in this Character, Setting, Plot Chart
help you analyze the story structure of *Lost City*?

 At Home: Have the student use the chart to retell the story.

© Macmillan/McGraw-Hill

Name _____

As I read, I will pay attention to the pronunciation of city names, pauses, and intonation.

	Abdullah (Ahb-DUL-lah) loosened his black-and-white
4	head covering. Another grueling day of work was under way.
14	His job was to help remove dirt from ancient tombs, or
25	graves. Abdullah looked around the excavation site and tried
34	to count all of the exposed graves. But he soon gave up.
46	"There are too many of them," he thought. "Besides, if
56	Sheik Hamoudi (Shayk hah-MOOD-ee) catches me counting
61	graves instead of working, he will send me away." Abdullah
71	threw himself into removing dirt, but while he worked,
80	he secretly dreamed of discovering a hidden treasure.
88	Sheik Hamoudi was the foreman on the site. He had
98	worked for the Englishman for a long time. For the past
109	week, the Sheik had been the boss while the Englishman and
120	his wife were away in Baghdad. He treated his workers fairly,
131	and yet he frightened Abdullah when he yelled. Abdullah had
141	grown up in the south of Iraq and had never been more than
154	a few miles from his village. 160

Comprehension Check

1. What words would you use to describe Abdullah? **Character, Setting, Plot**

2. What does Abdullah dream of finding? **Character, Setting, Plot**

	Words Read	–	Number of Errors	=	Words Correct Score
First Read		–		=	
Second Read		–		=	

At Home: Help the student read the passage, paying attention to the goal at the top of the page.

© Macmillan/McGraw-Hill

Social studies includes information about government, economics, geography, and history. Here are some special features that might help you use a social studies textbook.

a. **Table of Contents**—lists the book's units and chapters and their page numbers

b. **Headings and Subheadings**—identifies the contents of the page, section, or paragraph

c. **Glossary**—defines specific terms used in the text

d. **Index**—alphabetical list of subjects in the book with their page numbers

e. **Captions for Photographs**—often provide information about the subject

Answer the questions by writing the letter of the correct feature.

1. Where would you look for the beginning page number for Chapter 3? ____

2. Where would you look if you wanted to find information on Julius Caesar? ____

3. Where would you look to find out what the word *triumvirate* means? ____

4. Where would you look to find out what the article on page 156 concerns? ____

5. Where would you look to locate information on ancient Rome? ____

6. Where would you find information about a photograph of The Grand Canyon? ____

7. Where could you look to find the date of the beginning of World War I? ____

8. Where would you find the definition of *treaty*? ____

9. Where would you find further information about a specific topic? ____

10. Where would you find the page number of the beginning of a chapter on Japan? ____

© Macmillan/McGraw-Hill

At Home: Take turns giving directions from one place to another that your family visits. Ask the other person to guess where you will end up.

Compound words are words that consist of two or more words joined together. They can be hyphenated, closed, or open. If you are not sure how to write a compound word, look it up in the dictionary.

sister-in-law   everybody   roller skate

You can use the separate parts of compound words to determine their meaning.

under + growth = undergrowth
Low plants on the floor of a forest.

A. Identify the separate words that make up each compound word. Explain how they create the meaning of the word.

1. foretold _____

_____

_____

2. snowcapped _____

_____

_____

3. stonework _____

_____

_____

4. staircase _____

_____

_____

Write a sentence using a compound word. You may use one listed, or you may choose one on your own.

5. _____

_____

At Home: Have the student create three compound words of his or her own, along with definitions for these words.

Lost City • **Grade 6/Unit 1**   13

© Macmillan/McGraw-Hill

A common way to spell a **long vowel** sound is to use the pattern: vowel-consonant-silent *e.* Some examples: *gate, hide, eve, lone, mute.* There are also other ways to form long vowel sounds. The letter *y* can stand for the long *i* sound, as in *fly.* Two vowels together are called a diphthong and can stand for one sound. For example, the *ea* in *mean* stands for the long *e* sound. Other diphthongs that stand for long vowel sounds include *ee, ai,* and *oa.*

Look at each item. Fill in the missing vowel(s) to spell the sound. Then write the complete word in the space.

Vowels and Diphthongs

| a | e | i | o | u | y | ee | ea | ai | oa |

1. st____m   long *e*   _____

2. f____n____   long *i*   _____

3. f____nt   long *a*   _____

4. h____g____   long *u*   _____

5. c____cle   long *i*   _____

6. l____n   long *o*   _____

7. n____l   long *a*   _____

8. r____d   long *e*   _____

9. enc____clopedia   long *i*   _____

10. d____m____   long *o*   _____

At Home: Choose one sound spelled by a vowel or diphthong. Write a list that includes as many words that fit the pattern as you can.

© Macmillan/McGraw-Hill

Name _____

A. Write the vocabulary word that matches each clue.

> altered   erode   absorb   concentrated   innovations

1. This is what happens to ice when it melts. It means "changed."

   _____

2. This is another word for inventions or changes. _____

3. Things that are really packed together are called this. You can buy orange juice in this form. _____

4. Water and wind wear away at rocks and soil over time to do this.

   _____

5. A sponge or a paper towel can do this with liquid. _____

B. Write a sentence of your own using vocabulary words from the list above.

6. _____

   _____

7. _____

   _____

8. _____

   _____

9. _____

   _____

10. _____

   _____

© Macmillan/McGraw-Hill

Name _____

Read the passages. Then list the main idea and three supporting details for each one.

Science is all around us. Due to scientific research, we are able to communicate through the Internet and cell phones. Every time we bake something, we are participating in a scientific process. Our baked goods are new substances formed from a variety of single substances. Look around you. Many of the objects surrounding you, such as plastic or metal products, are the results of much scientific research and study.

Main Idea: _____

Supporting Details: _____

_____

_____

_____

Medicine helps us improve the quality of our lives. If you have a headache, you can take medicine to ease the pain. If you have an infection, a doctor can give you medicine to heal it. Without medicine, your infection could be deadly. In addition, doctors and researchers help people fight diseases with the help of vaccinations and antibiotics. Measles, tuberculosis, and polio are not nearly as threatening as they were 100 years ago because of medicine.

Main Idea: _____

_____

Supporting Details: _____

_____

_____

_____

© Macmillan/McGraw-Hill

Gecko Glue, Cockroach Scouts, and
Spider Silk Bridges • **Grade 6/Unit 1**

At Home: Have the student write a short paragraph about science. Have him or her ask a friend or family member to identify the main idea and supporting details.

As you read *Gecko Glue, Cockroach Scouts, and Spider Silk Bridges,* **fill in the Main Idea Web.**

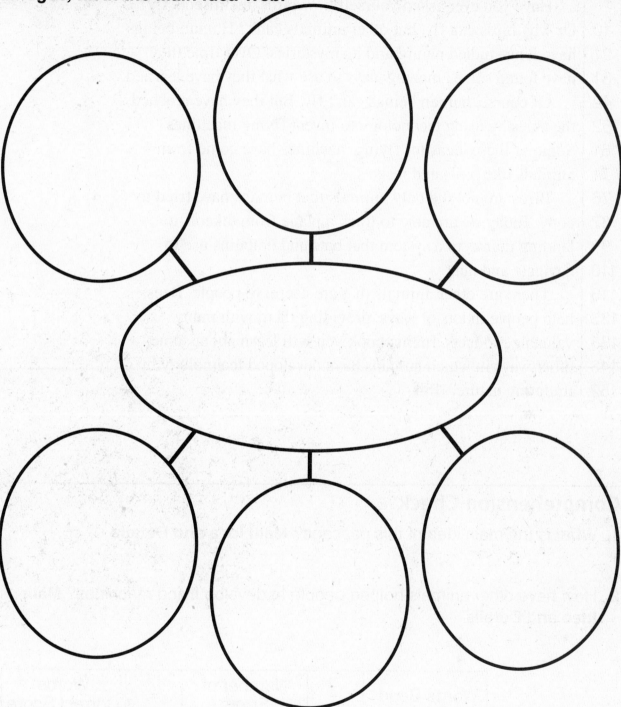

How does the information you wrote in this Main Idea Web help you make inferences and analyze the story structure of *Gecko Glue, Cockroach Scouts, and Spider Silk Bridges*?

At Home: Have the student use the chart to retell the story.

Gecko Glue, Cockroach Scouts, and
Spider Silk Bridges • **Grade 6/Unit 1**   17

© Macmillan/McGraw-Hill

Name _____

As I read, I will pay attention to the tempo.

	Have you ever asked yourself how birds and insects fly?
10	Or why birds can fly, but other animals can't? Human beings
21	have long studied nature and its mysteries. Over time they
31	have found some amazing ways to use what they have learned.
42	Of course, human beings can't fly. But they have reached
52	the skies by using technology to invent flying machines.
61	Some of these ideas for flying machines have come from
71	animals like birds and insects.
76	Birds are not the only animals that humans have tried to
87	copy. Today we are able to track a plane from takeoff to
99	landing thanks to a system that bats and dolphins use to
110	navigate and hunt.
113	There are other animals that are useful to people. Bees
123	help people in lots of ways, providing them with many
133	valuable products. In this book you will learn about some
143	other ways in which humans have developed technology by
152	imitating nature. 154

Comprehension Check

1. What is the main idea of this passage? **Main Idea and Details**

2. How have other animals helped people to develop flying machines? **Main Idea and Details**

	Words Read	–	Number of Errors	=	Words Correct Score
First Read		–		=	
Second Read		–		=	

© Macmillan/McGraw-Hill

At Home: Help the student read the passage, paying attention to the goal at the top of the page.

A library lists all its books, DVDs, and other materials in a card catalog. There are three cards in the card catalog for each book: an author card, a title card, and a subject card. If you know the author, the title, or the subject, you can flip through the appropriate section of the catalog.

An electronic catalog works the same way. However, you can also search by key words. For instance, you can enter an author's name and a subject, or even two or more subjects like *elephants* and *Indian*. An electronic search result will give you a numbered list of titles. Type in the number of the book and press enter. A screen for that particular book will come up, and give you the same information that you would find in a card catalog. It will also tell you if the book is available.

Look at the information on the following card. Then answer the questions below.

J292.13M	Press, Geraldine. *Greek Myths*. Illustrated by Eirene Zagoreas. New York, Children's Publishers, 2003. 208 p. illus. Includes famous Greek myths, retold for younger readers. 1. Literature 2. Mythology 3. Ancient Greece

1. What key words could you use to find this book? _____

   _____

2. Which row would house this book?

   a. J123.93–J292.01   b. J567.93–J890.23   c. J189.32–J301.78

3. What do you need to know to find this book? _____

   _____

4. What kind of work is this? _____

© Macmillan/McGraw-Hill

At Home: At home or at the library, use an online catalog to look up several books using different key words.

Gecko Glue, Cockroach Scouts, and
Spider Silk Bridges • **Grade 6/Unit 1**

19

Name _____

When you read, you should use the surrounding text, which often gives you **definitions** in context, to help you determine the meaning of unfamiliar vocabulary. Just as its name implies, this kind of context clue actually states the meaning of the unfamiliar word.

Underline the definitions you find in the sentences. Write a sentence of your own using the defined word from each sentence.

1. Astronauts used a powerful telescope to find out more about the cosmos, another name for the universe.

   _____

   _____

2. The scientists at Mission Control, the place where the trip was supervised, were in constant contact with the astronauts who planned the repair of the telescope.

   _____

   _____

3. So that the mission, the trip planned to fix the telescope, could succeed, the damaged part had to be replaced.

   _____

   _____

4. When the Endeavor was in place, the shuttle's robotic, or mechanical, arm was used to grab the damaged telescope.

   _____

   _____

5. Crew members left the shuttle through a small room with two hatches, or doors.

   _____

   _____

© Macmillan/McGraw-Hill

At Home: Taking turns, one partner gives a word and a context clue and the other person makes up a sentence.

The long *e* sound can be spelled by either **ei** or **ie.** The long *a* sound can be spelled by *ei*. To remember how to spell words with *ei* or *ie*, memorize the following sentence:

Place the *i* before *e* except after *c* or when sounding like *a* as in *neighbor* and *weigh.*

A. Read the sentences. Circle the words that contain the *ie* or *ei* digraphs. Then, in the space, write whether the sound is long *e* or long *a*.

1. The researcher mixed eight chemicals together. _____

2. Field work can help find the medicine that will work. _____

3. Researchers must yield to signs of danger when testing medicine.

   _____

4. They must weigh everything carefully. _____

5. Before they receive a new assignment, they must make thorough notes on

   the last one. _____

B. Fill in the missing letters in each sentence.

6. The laboratory has many vents in the c_____ling to prevent dangerous gases from building up.

7. Researchers wear goggles as a way to sh_____ld their eyes from laboratory chemicals.

8. Chemicals shipped by fr_____ght have to be handled with caution.

© Macmillan/McGraw-Hill

At Home: Together, find other words that have long *e* or long *a* spelled with *ie* or *ei*.

Gecko Glue, Cockroach Scouts, and
Spider Silk Bridges • **Grade 6/Unit 1**

21

Name _____

A. Complete each sentence with a vocabulary word.

chameleon	rummaged	scrounging	pathetic
undetected	generosity	ricocheting	famine

1. Many folk tale characters are known for their kindness and

   _____.

2. African folk tales often feature insect and animal characters, such as a

   spider or a _____.

3. My grandmother _____ through her attic to find her favorite
   book from her childhood.

4. At one point in the story, the children were so hungry they were

   _____ for food.

5. The children in the story were very brave, but the enemy was

   _____.

B. Write sentences of your own, using the remaining vocabulary words.

6. _____

   _____

7. _____

   _____

8. _____

   _____

© Macmillan/McGraw-Hill

Name _____

In stories and in real life, one event can make another event occur. For example, if your alarm does not go off then you might be late for school. The first event is the **cause**, and the second event is the **effect**. Authors use signal words or phrases such as *as a result, so, therefore, because, due to,* and *then* to show the relationships between events.

Read the following article. Underline the signal words or phrases that show the relationships between events. Then write the cause and effect of each situation as indicated by the signal words.

Passing on traditions is very important to some families because they feel it keeps family memories alive. When an older relative tells the story of his father's immigration to America, he is passing on part of the family tradition. Traditions also accompany holiday gatherings. Every year special events, such as holiday dinners and celebrations, take place. As a result, familiarity with the events are passed on to the younger generations. Then these youngsters grow up and pass on their awareness of traditions. Therefore, family tradition survives through the centuries.

1. cause _____

   effect _____

2. cause _____

   _____

   effect _____

3. cause _____

   effect _____

   _____

4. cause _____

   effect _____

   _____

© Macmillan/McGraw-Hill

At Home: Together, discuss family traditions. Which are the student's favorites? Why? Which tradition will he or she be likely to continue?

Name _____

As you read *The Magic Gourd*, fill in the Cause and Effect Chart.

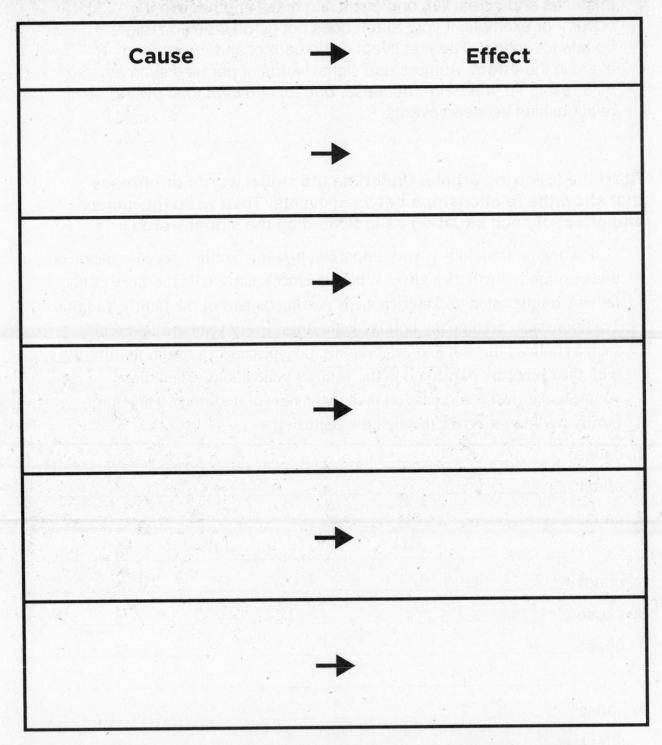

Cause	→	Effect

How does the information you wrote in this Cause and Effect Chart help
you make inferences and analyze the story structure of *The Magic Gourd*?

At Home: Have the student use the chart to retell the story.

© Macmillan/McGraw-Hill

Name _____

As I read, I will pay attention to punctuation.

	The Navajo (NAH-vah-hoh) Indians call themselves the
6	*Dineh* (dee-NAY). In Navajo, their name means "The People."
14	Over 255,000 Navajos live in the United States today. Their
23	nation is the largest in the country.
30	For generations the Navajo have made beautiful weavings,
38	baskets, and jewelry. Their arts reflect their traditions, their
47	history, and their modern life.
52	Centuries ago, the Navajo settled in a part of the Southwest
63	now called the Four Corners. It's called that because the
73	borders of four states meet in one spot.
81	The Four Corners area has beautiful canyons, mesas, rivers,
90	and rock formations. But the high desert climate is harsh and
101	dry. The Navajo lived in hogans. They moved often to find
112	grass for their sheep and horses. When the climate permitted,
122	they planted corn, squash, and melons. At times, on the brink
133	of **famine,** they have to be good farmers to get by.
144	In 1868, the United States and the Navajo signed a treaty.
154	The treaty promised them their own government, called the
163	Navajo Nation. It also created the huge Navajo Reservation in
173	the Four Corners area. 177

Comprehension Check

1. How does the climate affect the Navajo? **Cause and Effect**

2. Why is art important to the Navajo? **Draw Conclusions**

	Words Read	−	Number of Errors	=	Words Correct Score
First Read		−		=	
Second Read		−		=	

At Home: Help the student read the passage, paying attention to the goal at the top of the page

The Magic Gourd • Grade 6/Unit I   **25**

© Macmillan/McGraw-Hill

A **time line** organizes information chronologically, or in time order. Time lines are divided into spans of years. The time moves from the earliest on the left to the latest on the right. Events are listed on the time line in the year they occurred.

Use the time line below to answer the questions.

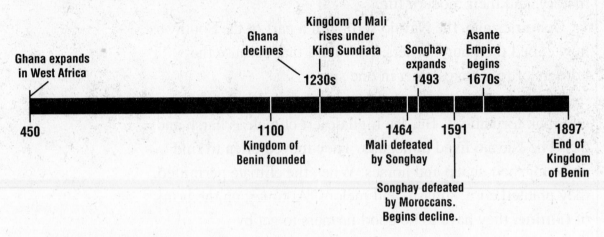

1. Which is the earliest entry on the time line?

   _____

2. About what year did Ghana begin to decline?

   _____

3. About how long did Mali exist?

   _____

4. Which is the longest-lived kingdom on the time line?

   _____

5. When were the Songhay defeated?

   _____

6. When did the Asante Empire begin?

   _____

At Home: Together, make a time line of the student's life. Divide the time line into year segments, and list major events for each year.

© Macmillan/McGraw-Hill

When you read, you should use the context, or surrounding words, to help you determine the meaning of unfamiliar vocabulary. One kind of context clue is **restatement,** in which the meaning of a word is restated after the word appears. Look at the example:

The country was afflicted by famine. It suffered from an extreme scarcity of food.

The meaning of the word *famine* is restated in the sentence that follows it.

Read each sentence. Circle the word whose meaning is restated. Then write the meaning on the line.

1. Passing on cultural traditions is important to Malians, the people who live

   in Mali. _____

2. Often storytelling is accompanied by djembes, which are drums that people play as others tell stories, dance, or sing.

   _____

3. The Dogon, a tribe of people in Mali who live at the base of the Bandiagara Cliffs, have rituals of their own.

   _____

4. The Dama dance, which is religious, is part of the Dogon tradition.

   _____

5. Part of the Dama dance is done on stilts, which are long poles people can stand on to mimic the long legs of a water bird.

   _____

At Home: Together, discuss various dancers and dances from different cultures that you know about.

The Magic Gourd • **Grade 6/Unit 1** | 27

© Macmillan/McGraw-Hill

Name _____

When a vowel is followed by the letter *r* it has a different sound than a vowel that is short or long, for example, the sound *âr* in *cart.* This is called an **r-controlled vowel.** The *r*-controlled sound can be spelled in different ways, for example: *surf, bird,* or *work.*

Read each clue. Provide an answer that uses an *r*-controlled vowel sound. Then use each word you found in a sentence.

1. Something that is ripped is this. _____

   _____

   _____

2. This is on the side of your head. _____

   _____

   _____

3. You can play games, eat hot dogs, and see farm animals here.

   _____

   _____

   _____

4. This is something you can do in the ocean. _____

   _____

   _____

5. This is the opposite of far. _____

   _____

   _____

6. You can brush it, curl it, or put it in braids. _____

   _____

   _____

At Home: Together, make up a limerick or a poem that uses pairs of *r*-controlled vowels.

© Macmillan/McGraw-Hill

Name _____

Write each word next to its definition.

vital	conserve	sedated	analyzing
speculated	embedded	dehydrated	propelled

1. examining carefully and in detail in order to understand something _____

2. moved or driven forward _____

3. avoid waste; save or preserve _____

4. of greatest importance _____

5. medicated to calm or go to sleep _____

6. thought of reasons or answers _____

7. dried out due to lost water or moisture _____

8. set into surrounding matter _____

Write four sentences using one of the vocabulary words in each sentence.

9. _____

_____

10. _____

_____

11. _____

_____

12. _____

_____

© Macmillan/McGraw-Hill

Read the paragraph. Then answer the questions.

The Florida Everglades are home to many birds, reptiles, and mammals. The Everglades provide a variety of habitats. They are vital to the wildlife they support, supplying particular environmental conditions that can be found only in the Everglades. Birds and other animals are protected by the sawgrass prairies. Crocodiles and alligators live together in the swamps and water. People must protect and preserve this land in order to nurture and protect the wildlife that make the Everglades their home.

1. What is the main idea of this paragraph?

_____

_____

2. Where is the main idea of this paragraph located?

_____

3. Why do you think it is located there?

_____

4. What purpose do the first and second sentences serve?

_____

5. Why are the Everglades vital to wildlife?

_____

_____

At Home: Discuss the main idea and details of another passage with the student.

© Macmillan/McGraw-Hill

As you read *Interrupted Journey*, fill in the Main Idea Web.

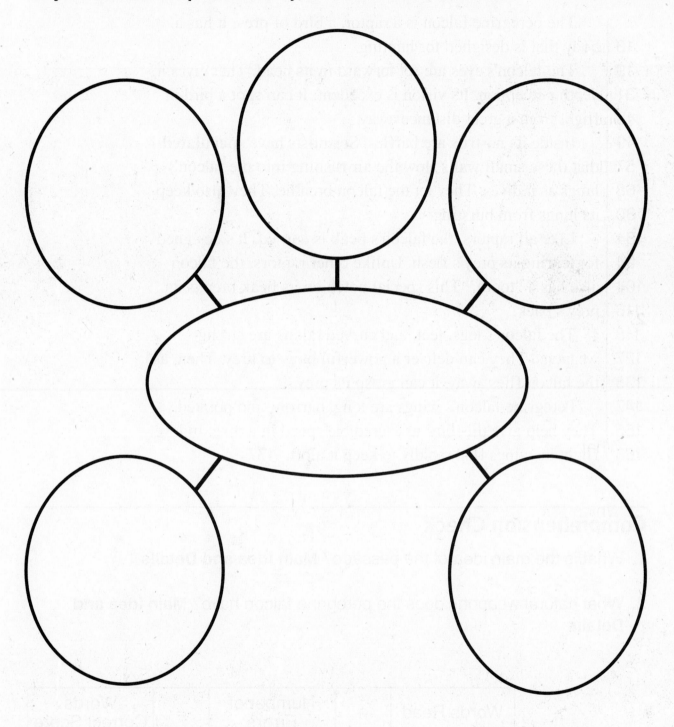

© Macmillan/McGraw-Hill

How does the information you wrote in this Main Idea Web help you make inferences and analyze the story structure of *Interrupted Journey*?

At Home: Have the student use the chart to retell the story.

Interrupted Journey • Grade 6/Unit 1   31

Name _____

As I read, I will pay attention to tempo.

13	The peregrine falcon is a raptor, a bird of prey. It has a body that is designed for hunting.
19	The falcon's eyes are set forward in its head. That gives it
31	depth perception. Its vision is excellent. It can spot a bird in
43	flight from a great distance away.
49	Inside its nostrils are baffles. Scientists have **speculated**
57	that these small walls slow the air rushing into the falcon's
68	lungs as it dives. They let the falcon breathe. They also keep
80	its lungs from bursting.
84	Like all raptors, the falcon's beak is curved. It's designed
94	for tearing its prey's flesh. Unlike other raptors, the falcon
104	also has a "tooth." This special notch on its beak breaks its
116	prey's back.
118	The falcon's legs, feet, and curved talons are strong
127	weapons. They can deliver a powerful blow to prey. Then, as
138	the falcon flies away, it can grasp its prey.
147	Peregrine falcon's wings are long, narrow, and pointed.
155	They help give this bird its incredible speed in a dive. In level
168	flight its wings flap rapidly to keep it aloft. 177

Comprehension Check

1. What is the main idea of the passage? **Main Idea and Details**

2. What natural weapons does the peregrine falcon have? **Main Idea and Details**

	Words Read	–	Number of Errors	=	Words Correct Score
First Read		–		=	
Second Read		–		=	

© Macmillan/McGraw-Hill

At Home: Help the student read the passage, paying attention to the goal at the top of the page

Name _____

> Free verse is poetry with irregular lines. It lacks a metrical pattern and a rhyme scheme.
>
> **Alliteration** is the repetition of initial consonant sounds.
>
> **Imagery** is the use of words to create a picture in the reader's mind.

Read the free-verse poem. Then answer the questions.

> Creeping and crouching,
> The snow leopard depends on stealth.
> He looks at his lunch having lunch.
> Slowly the snow leopard approaches,
> only to pounce!
> Alas, he won't have his lunch now—
> his four-legged lunch leapt to safety.

1. What sound is repeated in the first line?

_____

In the last line? _____

2. What imagery does the poem create in your mind?

_____

_____

Think about a scene from nature. Write your own free-verse poem. Use alliteration and imagery to capture the scene.

_____

_____

_____

_____

_____

_____

© Macmillan/McGraw-Hill

At Home: Take turns finding words that show alliteration and imagery.

Name _____

Using analogies requires you to understand how words relate to each other.

Analogies are written like this: up : down :: conserve : waste.

They are read like this: "*Up* is to *down* as *conserve* is to *waste.*"

One relationship that is often used is opposites, or **antonyms,** as in the example given above. Choose the best word to complete the analogy.

A. Circle the letter of the correct answer.

1. open : closed :: wild : _____

   a. savage   **b.** quiet   **c.** tame   **d.** barbaric

2. advance : retreat :: comedy : _____

   a. tragedy   **b.** music   **c.** jokes   **d.** laughter

3. agree : disagree :: feast : _____

   a. Thanksgiving   **b.** famine   **c.** festival   **d.** hunger

4. remain : leave :: allow : _____

   a. permit   **b.** decide   **c.** request   **d.** prohibit

5. defeat : victory :: lazy : _____

   a. weary   **b.** ambitious   **c.** aggressive   **d.** decent

B. Write three analogies, using antonyms, of your own.

6. _____

7. _____

8. _____

At Home: Play a game in which the student gives a word and you make up an antonym for that word. Take turns.

© Macmillan/McGraw-Hill

> **Compound words** are words that are made of up two or more words.
>
> apple + sauce = applesauce
>
> When you find compound words, you can use the single words that make them up to help you pronounce the larger word. For example, look at the word *homework.* First, you need to determine that the word is made up of the words *home* and *work.* Then you can apply what you know about pronunciation to sound out the word. You know the VCe uses a silent *e* to make a long *o* sound in *home.* And you know that a vowel followed by an *r* has a specific *r*-controlled sound.

Read each compound word. Put a slash through the word to divide it into single words. Then write a sentence using the word.

1. everybody _____

2. downpour _____

_____

3. flashbulb _____

_____

4. something _____

_____

5. weekend _____

_____

6. mountainside _____

7. beachfront _____

_____

8. wildlife _____

_____

At Home: Have the student think of as many words as he or she can that are compound words. Then work together to make the list as long as possible.

Interrupted Journey • Grade 6/Unit 1   35

Name _____

Complete the crossword puzzle with the clues below.

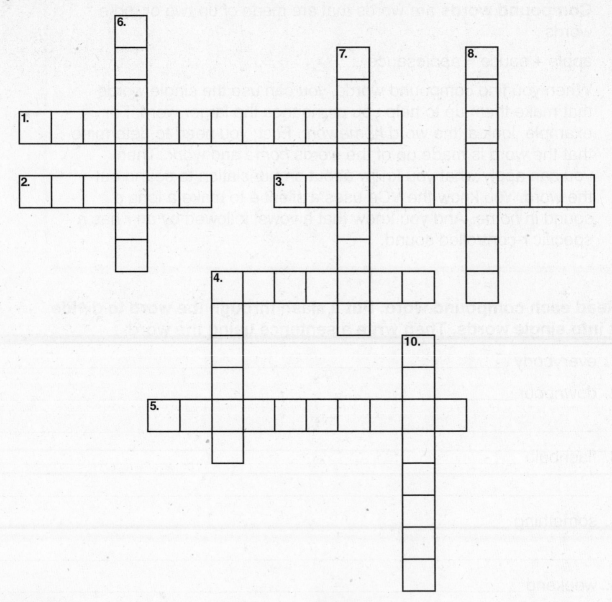

Across

1. place where two or more roads meet
2. secluded
3. to assume to be true without complete proof
4. changed
5. looking desperately for

Down

4. take in
6. predicted
7. established way of action
8. picked through
10. save

© Macmillan/McGraw-Hill

Name _____

A. Write each vocabulary word from the box next to the appropriate clue.

engulf	abruptly	withstood	vegetation	erode

1. synonym of quickly _____

2. to cover or swallow up someone or something _____

3. the plant life or the plants that cover an area _____

4. to wear away _____

5. resisted the effect _____

B. Write the correct vocabulary word from the box in the following sentences.

propelled	innovations	undetected	generosity	dehydrated

6. Raquel's _____ helped raise more money than expected.

7. Spencer's _____ helped improve the process.

8. During hide and seek, Kim went _____.

9. Grapes are _____ by sunlight to make raisins.

10. The wind _____ Sara's sailboat across the water.

© Macmillan/McGraw-Hill

Name _____

Fill in each blank with a vocabulary word.

> inscribed   resemblance   postmarked   enthralled
>
> regulation   grouchy   embarrassment   pennant

Our quiz team would never have won the _____ without

working together. At our first practice, everyone was _____

because it was so early in the morning. Jenny suffered from

_____ because she forgot the answers to most of the

science questions. Hiroshi was _____ with the buzzers. Keila

refused to wear the _____ uniform. Finally, our coach opened

a letter. It was _____ July 1972. _____ on the

envelope was the name of my favorite game show host. He had written to our

coach for advice when he was young. Our coach explained that we had no

chance of winning if we did not have even a _____ to a team.

We needed team spirit! Once we found it, we were able to cooperate and

to win.

Choose two vocabulary words. Write sentences using these words.

1. _____

_____

_____

2. _____

_____

_____

© Macmillan/McGraw-Hill

Name _____

Read the story and answer the questions.

The basketball team could not win a game. It did not make any sense. They had many good players. They had a lot of experience. When Coach Grimley watched the Falcons play their first game, he immediately understood why they could not win. Everyone wanted to be a star. At the next practice, the coach explained that no one would be a star if they did not show some team spirit and support each other. In practices during the next week, all the team members did was pass the ball to other players who were in a better position to score points. When the next game came around, the Falcons won!

1. Why could the Falcons not win?

_____

_____

2. What is implied by the sentence, "Everyone wanted to be a star"?

_____

_____

3. What can you infer about Coach Grimley's approach to basketball?

_____

_____

4. What can you infer from the Falcons' winning?

_____

_____

© Macmillan/McGraw-Hill

At Home: Show team spirit as you take on a task around the house. Ask all household members to participate.

Name _____

As you read *How Tía Lola Came to ~~Visit~~/Stay*, fill in the
Inferences Chart.

Text Clues and Prior Knowledge	Inference

How does the information you wrote in this Inferences Chart help you
make inferences about *How Tía Lola Came to ~~Visit~~/Stay*?

© Macmillan/McGraw-Hill

At Home: Have the student use the chart
to retell the story.

As I read, I will pay attention to pauses, stops, and intonation.

	Jenna turns her head to look at the pennant on the wall
12	above her bed. It's from her old school basketball team, the
23	Wilson Wildcats. Jenna had been a star forward on the team,
34	and some of her best friends had played, too. Then again,
45	Jenna had had a lot of friends at Wilson. She had lived in
58	the same small town her whole life. Being at Wilson was like
70	going to school with your extended family.
77	Now Jenna, her brother Sean, and her parents had moved
87	into a new neighborhood in a big city. There were three times
99	as many students at Eastern Middle School as there were at
110	Wilson. Jenna let out a loud sigh. How was she ever going to
123	make friends?
125	After dinner the night before the first day, Jenna and her
136	brother Sean play one-on-one basketball in the driveway.
144	They've been shooting baskets together as long as Jenna can
154	remember. Their evening games have always been Jenna's
162	favorite part of the day. 167

Comprehension Check

1. What kind of relationship do Jenna and her brother have? **Make Inferences**

2. Why was Wilson like an extended family for Jenna? **Cause and Effect**

	Words Read	–	Number of Errors	=	Words Correct Score
First Read		–		=	
Second Read		–		=	

At Home: Help the student read the passage, paying attention to the goal at the top of the page.

How Tía Lola Came to ~~Visit~~/Stay
Grade 6/Unit 2

41

© Macmillan/McGraw-Hill

An **almanac** contains general information about various topics. Almanacs are published yearly and contain statistics for the previous year.

Almanacs are filled with up-to-date information in a concise format. The index is the organizer for the almanac. Almanacs also appear online and they often have indexes that are links to the information you are seeking.

Use the almanac index to answer the questions.

Animals	First Aid	Mortality Statistics	Taxes
Architecture	Foreign Phrases	Newspapers	Time Zones
Baseball	Geography	Nutrition	Tropical Storms
Calendars	Governors, U.S.	Olympics	Volcanoes
Cities, World	Holidays	Presidents	Weather
Endangered Species	Hurricanes	Refugees	Writing/Language

1. Under which three headings would you probably find information about Hurricane Andrew? _____

2. Where could you learn the days of the week in French?

   _____

3. Where could you find out who designed a famous building?

   _____

4. Where would you find out what public official is the head of your state?

   _____

5. Where could you find out what time it is in Sydney, Australia?

   _____

6. Which two headings might have information about bald eagles?

   _____

At Home: Together, think of other facts you might find in an almanac and make a list of them.

© Macmillan/McGraw-Hill

Practice

Name _____

Vocabulary Strategy:
Inflectional Endings

Change each sentence to the past tense by adding the inflectional ending -ed to appropriate action verbs.

1. Kim and Joey play together after school on Mondays.

_____

_____

2. The class members work together to decorate the gym.

_____

_____

3. Even though they might fail to win the game, the players always hope to win the next one.

_____

_____

4. Every person creates a part of the presentation.

_____

5. When we walk on a school trip, we cross the street together as a class.

_____

_____

6. Jamal helps his friends build a model car.

_____

7. Jumanda saves her money to buy a new computer.

_____

8. Yoshi likes to read aloud in class.

_____

At Home: Discuss how meanings change when you add the inflectional ending -ed to different action verbs.

How Tía Lola Came to ~~Visit~~/Stay
Grade 6/Unit 2   43

© Macmillan/McGraw-Hill

Name _____

Plurals are often formed by adding the letter *s* to the end of a word.
    dog + s = dogs   cat + s = cats
Some words have to be changed slightly to form plurals.
    wolf   wolves   knife   knives
Sometimes, the letter *s* does not make an /s/ sound. Instead, it makes the /z/ sound.

A. Write the words in the sentences that have an *s* that makes a /z/ sound.

1. Team spirit is not just for baseball teams. _____

2. You and your classmates can work together to meet goals.

   _____

3. Team spirit is about working together as equals. _____

4. You can work together to solve problems. _____

5. Members of a team do their best to make their plans successful.

   _____

6. Teams can succeed if they use the strengths of each member.

   _____

B. Write some sentences of your own that contain plurals that have the /z/ sound.

7. _____

   _____

8. _____

   _____

9. _____

   _____

10. _____

   _____

© Macmillan/McGraw-Hill

At Home: Practice writing your own sentences using plurals that make the /z/ sound.

Name _____

A. Write each vocabulary word on the line next to its definition.

| spicy | undone | vigil | ravaged |
| marveled | broadcast | unsatisfactory | calculations |

1. _____ mathematical reckoning or figuring

2. _____ came apart or unfastened

3. _____ a period of remaining awake to guard

4. _____ transmitted by radio or television

5. _____ laid waste to, destroyed

6. _____ zesty; flavored with spices

7. _____ became filled with wonder or astonishment

8. _____ not good enough to meet a need or desire

B. Write four sentences of your own. Use at least one vocabulary word in each sentence.

9. _____

_____

10. _____

_____

11. _____

_____

12. _____

_____

© Macmillan/McGraw-Hill

Name _____

Study the diagram and answer the questions.

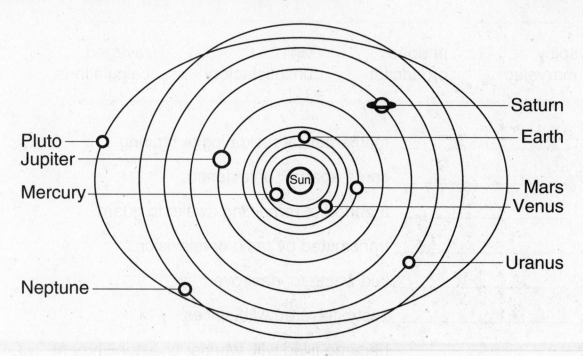

1. What can you infer about Saturn's climate in relation to Earth's?

   _____

   _____

2. Which is likely the hottest planet in our solar system? Explain.

   _____

   _____

3. Which planet is likely to be the coldest planet in the solar system? Explain.

   _____

   _____

4. Which planets would we most likely be able to see in our night sky with no

   telescope? Explain. _____

   _____

   _____

The Night of the Pomegranate
Grade 6/Unit 2

At Home: Together, spend some time at night looking at
the sky to locate planets and constellations.

© Macmillan/McGraw-Hill

Name _____

As you read *The Night of the Pomegranate,* fill in the
Inferences Diagram.

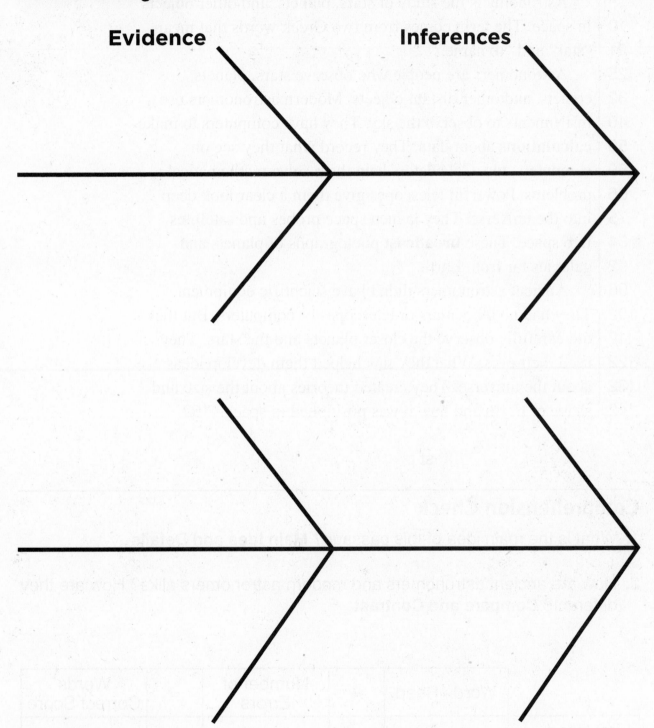

Evidence   **Inferences**

How does the information you wrote in this Inferences Diagram help you
monitor comprehension of *The Night of the Pomegranate*?

At Home: Have the student use the chart to retell the story.

The Night of the Pomegranate
Grade 6/Unit 2

47

© Macmillan/McGraw-Hill

Name _____

As I read, I will pay attention to punctuation.

	Astronomy is the study of stars, planets, and other objects
10	in space. The term comes from two Greek words that mean
21	"star" and "to name."
25	Astronomers are people who observe stars, planets,
32	comets, and other distant objects. Modern astronomers use
40	instruments to observe the sky. They have computers to make
50	**calculations** about data. They record what they see on
59	computers, too. Calculators help them solve mathematical
66	problems. Powerful telescopes give them a clear look deep
75	into the universe. They launch space probes and satellites
84	into space. These **broadcast** photographs of planets and
92	galaxies far from Earth.
96	Ancient astronomers didn't have scientific equipment.
102	They had no binoculars or telescopes or computers. But they
112	did carefully observe the closer planets and the stars. They
122	used their eyes. What they saw helped them develop ideas
132	about the universe. They created theories about the size and
142	shape of Earth and how it was positioned in space. 152

Comprehension Check

1. What is the main idea of this passage? **Main Idea and Details**

2. How are ancient astronomers and modern astronomers alike? How are they different? **Compare and Contrast**

	Words Read	–	Number of Errors	=	Words Correct Score
First Read		–		=	
Second Read		–		=	

© Macmillan/McGraw-Hill

At Home: Help the student read the passage, paying attention to the goal at the top of the page.

Graphs show information visually. They are used to compare things or to show how things change over time.

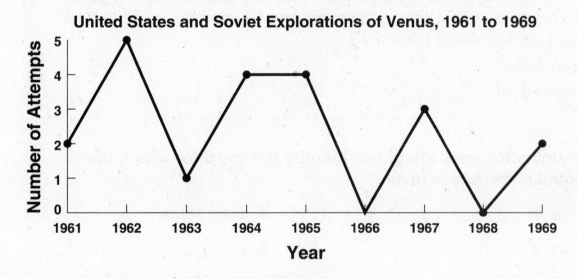

United States and Soviet Explorations of Venus, 1961 to 1969

Study the line graph. Answer the questions.

1. Which of the years had the fewest attempts to explore Venus?

_____

2. How many attempts were made during 1964 and 1965?

_____

3. Which year had the most attempts to explore Venus? How many?

_____

4. How many attempts were made during 1963?

_____

5. What trend does this line graph show over the time period given?

_____

_____

_____

© Macmillan/McGraw-Hill

At Home: Help the student plot some kind of change over time on a line graph.

The Night of the Pomegranate
Grade 6/Unit 2

49

Name _____

When you are unsure about a word's pronunciation, check the dictionary. A **pronunciation key** follows each word. If you are unsure about the symbols in the pronunciation key, check the table of contents of the dictionary. Most dictionaries have a guide to pronunciation. Use the pronunciation key and the guide to help you say the words correctly.

Example:
vigil **vij´-əl**

Pronunciation keys are given. Identify the word for which the pronunciation key is given.

1. vū´ ər _____

2. tel´ ə skōp _____

3. stär´ gāz´ _____

4. plan´ i ter´ē _____

5. nol´ ij _____

6. i klips´ _____

Write four sentences. Use one of the words from the list above in each sentence.

7. _____

_____

8. _____

_____

9. _____

_____

10. _____

_____

At Home: Help the student look up several words in a dictionary, in the library, or online for pronunciation guidance.

© Macmillan/McGraw-Hill

Name _____

When you add -ed or -ing to a word, you usually double the last consonant when the vowel that comes before the ending has a short sound.

trap + ed = trapped   trap + ing = trapping
shop + ed = shopped   shop + ing = shopping

You do not double the last consonant when the vowel that comes before it is long or when the word ends with more than one consonant. You just add the ending. If a word ends with a silent e, you drop the e before adding the ending.

peek + ed = peeked   peek + ing = peeking
rest + ed = rested   rest + ing = resting
time + ed = timed   time + ing = timing

There are also some exceptions to the rules above.

pilot + ed = piloted   pilot + ing = piloting
travel + ed = traveled   travel + ing = traveling

Read each word and add the endings -ed and -ing to each one. Follow the rules above.

1. open _____   6. trot _____

2. close _____   7. coat _____

3. hope _____   8. cook _____

4. hop _____   9. direct _____

5. wish _____   10. deliver _____

© Macmillan/McGraw-Hill

At Home: Together, write a story about any subject using several words with inflectional endings.

| administer | mitigate | devastating | evacuate | calamities |

A. Complete each sentence with a vocabulary word.

1. After _____ such as tornadoes or hurricanes, people and animals need help.

2. The damage from a natural disaster can be _____ to a community.

3. Often, people are warned of the coming storm and can _____ their homes before the storm arrives.

4. Volunteers help _____ the damage suffered by residents who lived through a storm.

5. Different groups _____ relief in many ways, providing food, shelter, and healthcare.

B. Write sentences of your own about natural disasters. Use a vocabulary word in each sentence.

6. _____

_____

7. _____

_____

8. _____

_____

9. _____

_____

10. _____

_____

© Macmillan/McGraw-Hill

Name _____

Read the article. Then answer the questions.

On December 26, 2004, a tsunami hit Southeast Asia. The tsunami, a result of an earthquake in the middle of the ocean, leveled beach resorts and coastal cities, and washed inland. It hit several countries in Southeast Asia, including Indonesia and Thailand. The tsunami washed away buildings, cars, animals, and people. The death toll from the natural disaster was over 200,000. Such a large tsunami hasn't been seen for thousands of years, if ever. Surviving residents now face the challenge of putting their homes, their cities, and their lives back together.

They are doing this with an overwhelming amount of aid. People from around the globe have worked together to help the victims of this natural disaster. From small children donating allowances to countries donating millions of dollars, people are pitching in to help. Musicians have performed concerts, and restaurants have hosted benefits. International relief organizations have played vital roles in assisting the victims. Now the challenge is to get the aid to the people who need it the most.

1. What generalization about this tsunami can you make from the information in the first paragraph? _____

   _____

2. What can you say about tsunamis in general?

   _____

3. What generalization can you make about people in disaster situations based on the second paragraph?

   _____

4. What can you say about people in general based on the information in the article? _____

5. What are some of the relief efforts that you have heard about or read about? List as many as you can.

   _____

© Macmillan/McGraw-Hill

At Home: Help the student discuss ways that ordinary people help others in the face of disasters.

As you read *Zoo Story*, fill in the Generalizations Chart.

Important Information	Generalization

How does the information you wrote in this Generalizations Chart help
you monitor comprehension of *Zoo Story*?

© Macmillan/McGraw-Hill

At Home: Have the student use the chart to retell the story.

Name _____

As I read, I will pay attention to the pronunciation of vocabulary and other difficult words.

	The Midwest floods hit Iowa in July 1993. On July 10 heavy
10	rains poured down on ground that was already soaked. The
20	next day, the rising Raccoon River flooded. River waters broke
30	through the levee protecting Iowa's capital city of Des Moines.
40	A levee is a man-made wall. Levees keep river waters from
51	flooding populated areas. But sometimes they fail.
58	The raging waters flooded Des Moines' water treatment plant.
66	The plant shut down. For 12 days 250,000 people in
75	Des Moines were without clean water for drinking. Residents
84	couldn't bathe, wash their clothes, or even flush their toilets.
94	There wasn't enough water to use in fighting fires. The mayor
105	of Des Moines shut down all but the most essential businesses.
116	Des Moines needed clean water—and fast. Soon help was there.
127	Help came from the Federal Emergency Management Agency,
134	or FEMA. FEMA goes in to help when the President of the
145	United States declares a place a disaster area. The agency tries
157	to **mitigate**, or help make better, some of the problems. It finds
169	people shelter. It repairs buildings and provides insurance
178	money. In Des Moines, FEMA took charge of getting fresh
188	water to the city. 192

Comprehension Check

1. Why is flooding a problem? **Make Generalizations**

2. How did FEMA help Des Moines? **Main Idea and Details**

	Words Read	–	Number of Errors	=	Words Correct Score
First Read		–		=	
Second Read		–		=	

© Macmillan/McGraw-Hill

At Home: Help the student read the passage, paying attention to the goal at the top of the page.

Name _____

When you need to research a topic, you can use a search engine to explore the Internet. You will need to think of key words to enter into the search box. Enter the words, click on search, and the search engine will find a list of Web sites. Each Web site listing will have a brief description and a Web address. Click on an underlined link to open a new Web page.

Best Web Browser | Hurricane Andrew | | Search |

1. Tropical Storm Center - **Hurricane Andrew**
   The Tropical Storm Center's main page on **Hurricane Andrew** of 1992
   http://www.tsc.gov
2. National Weather Home Page - **Hurricane Andrew**
   Hurricane Andrew a very destructive United States **hurricane**
   http://www.nationalweather.gov
3. U.S. Satellite Pictures - **Hurricane Andrew**
   Satellite pictures and upper-air data of **Hurricane Andrew**
   http://www.ussatellitepics.gov
4. Aftermath Photos - **Hurricane Andrew**
   Photographs of damage after Florida's worst hurricane
   http://www.andrewpics.com
5. 10 Years after **Hurricane Andrew**: America's Newspaper
   People's lives 10 years after the destructive **Hurricane Andrew**
   http://www.americasnewspaper.com

Use the search results to answer the questions.

1. Which key words were used to search for information? _____

2. Which sites might have information about the storm's origins?

   _____

   _____

3. Which national newspaper has an article on Andrew?

   _____

4. If you needed pictures, which sites would likely be most helpful?

   _____

5. If you wanted to search for the effects of Andrew on Miami, which keywords

   would you use? _____

© Macmillan/McGraw-Hill

At Home: Help the student search the Internet for information about relief efforts for a natural disaster.

Name _____

Read the paragraph. Answer the questions.

One of the most important things to remember when calamity strikes is not to panic. A panicky person cannot think clearly. A person who panics cannot maneuver through the obstacles presented by a disaster, such as a tornado or hurricane. Each kind of disaster requires a different action. For example, a tornado requires people to go to the center of a building, preferably a room with no windows, or a basement, and cover their heads. A hurricane, on the other hand, requires evacuation because the storm surge can flood areas. If the storm surge rises too high, people will be stranded on rooftops and unable to get to safety. In the event of an earthquake, people should get outside or stand in doorways for protection. Seismic activity causes the ground to shake and buildings to come toppling down in some cases. Regardless of the kind of natural disaster, a calm approach will allow you to think things through and act appropriately for the situation.

1. What does *maneuver* mean? _____

_____

2. Which clues helped you define *maneuver*? _____

_____

_____

3. What is a storm surge? _____

_____

4. Which clues helped you define *storm surge*? _____

_____

_____

5. What is seismic activity? _____

6. Which clues helped you define *seismic activity*? _____

_____

_____

At Home: Ask the student to write a sentence using the word *requires* along with a context clue to help define it.

Zoo Story • Grade 6/Unit 2   57

© Macmillan/McGraw-Hill

Name _____

The spellings *ou, oi, au,* and *oo* stand for a variety of sounds. For example, the *ou* in *found* is different from the *ou* in *fought*. The *ou* in *found* stands for the same sound as the *ou* in *sound*, while the *ou* in *fought* stands for the same sound as the *au* in *naughty*. The *oo* in *gloom* stands for a different sound from the *oo* in *book*. The *oi* sound is the most regular and is made by either the *oi* in *coil* or the *oy* in *boy*.

1. Circle the words in which *ou* stands for the same sound as in *foul*.

   boundary   loud   fought   bough   fountain   mount

2. Circle the words that have the same vowel sound as *naughty*.

   caught   bought   autumn   often   cough   laugh

3. Circle the words that have the same *oo* sound as in *gloom*.

   room   hook   boot   cook   foot   loot

Fill in each blank with *oi* or *oy* to spell a word.

4. b_____

5. s_____

6. _____ster

7. sp_____l

8. c_____l

9. n_____sy

10. b_____sterous

11. av_____d

12. cl_____stered

13. cl_____

14. depl_____

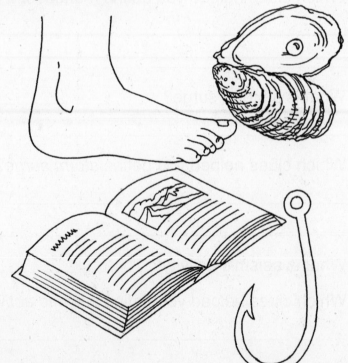

© Macmillan/McGraw-Hill

At Home: Together, list as many words as you can that have the sound /ou/ in them.

Name _____

Complete the crossword puzzle with words from the vocabulary list using the clues below.

coincidences   sweeten   phase   hobbled
sheepishly   prospered   sumptuous   mufflers

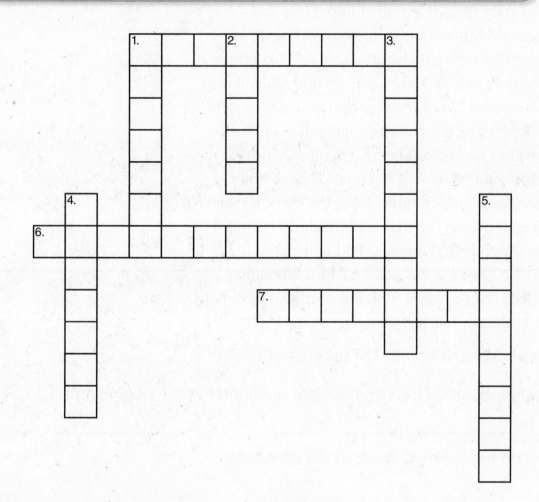

Across

1. extremely rich and magnificent
6. accidental events that seem to be connected
7. scarves

Down

1. to make more attractive
2. a part of something that changes
3. showing embarrassment
4. walked unsteadily
5. succeeded

© Macmillan/McGraw-Hill

Read the passage and answer the questions.

"The Bear and the Two Travelers"
A Fable by Aesop

Two men were traveling together, when a bear suddenly met them on their path. One of the men quickly climbed into a tree and concealed himself in the branches. The other, seeing that he would be attacked, fell flat on the ground. When the bear came up and nudged him with his snout, and smelled him all over, he held his breath and feigned the appearance of death as well as he could. The bear soon left him, for it is said bears will not touch a dead body. When the bear was quite gone, the other traveler descended from the tree, and jocularly inquired of his friend what the bear had whispered in his ear. "He gave me this advice," his companion replied. "Never travel with a friend who deserts you at the approach of danger."

Moral: Misfortune tests the sincerity of friends.

1. What problem do the two travelers encounter at the beginning?

   _____

2. How do the travelers react to the situation?

   _____

3. What problem arises for the second traveler?

   _____

   _____

4. Relate the moral of the story in your own words.

   _____

© Macmillan/McGraw-Hill

At Home: Together, identify and discuss a problem and possible solutions. Then decide which is the best solution.

As you read *Rumpelstiltskin's Daughter,* fill in the
Problem and Solution Chart.

Problem

Attempt		Outcome
	→	

Attempt		Outcome
	→	

Solution

How does the information you wrote in this Problem and Solution Chart
help you monitor comprehension of *Rumpelstiltskin's Daughter*?

© Macmillan/McGraw-Hill

At Home: Have the student use the chart to retell the story.

Rumpelstiltskin's Daughter
Grade 6/Unit 2

61

As I read, I will pay attention to tempo.

	Long ago in a land of forests and mountains, two kingdoms sat
12	side by side. One, on the borders of a forest, was inhabited by men
26	and women who lived and worked on farms and in villages. In this
39	place, the sun shone on most days and rain fell only when it was
53	really needed. As any traveler through the region could report, the
64	people there were always busy, usually happy, and never sad for
75	long.
76	The second kingdom, however, was hidden from sight. For it lay
87	mostly beneath a mountain whose base went so deep that it seemed
99	to reach almost to the fiery center of the earth. This was the
112	kingdom of the gnomes, and its ruler was one Beryl Hardstone.
123	Beryl was a princely sort, given his fabulous wealth. Beryl had
134	all the traits and powers of gnomes. He was small, bearded, and not
147	particularly handsome, at least in human terms. He could move
157	through solid earth as easily as through air. And he could carry
169	with him whatever he held in his hands. This was useful because,
181	in true gnome fashion, Beryl was a miner and he liked to take his
195	precious stones with him. 199

Comprehension Check

1. Why does the author compare the two kingdoms? **Author's Purpose**

2. What can you infer about the citizens who live in the second kingdom?
   Make Inferences

	Words Read	–	Number of Errors	=	Words Correct Score
First Read		–		=	
Second Read		–		=	

© Macmillan/McGraw-Hill

At Home: Help the student read the passage, paying attention to the goal at the top of the page.

A myth is a story that explains occurrences in nature through the intervention of gods and goddesses.

A **moral** is a practical lesson contained in the narrative.

Hyperbole is the deliberate use of exaggeration for emphasis. Myths sometimes use hyperbole to describe human weaknesses.

Now that you have read "The Golden Touch," you know how myths use hyperbole, explain natural occurrences, and teach a moral at the same time. Think of an explanation for a natural occurrence. Write your own myth about this occurrence. You can make up gods and goddesses, or you can borrow them from ancient cultures. Be sure that your myth not only explains an occurrence but also teaches a lesson, such as "It doesn't pay to be greedy" or "Be kind to everyone."

_____

_____

_____

_____

_____

_____

_____

_____

_____

_____

_____

_____

© Macmillan/McGraw-Hill

At Home: Together, make up a myth to explain why the wind blows or why something else occurs naturally.

Rumpelstiltskin's Daughter
Grade 6/Unit 2

63

An **idiom** is an expression whose meaning cannot necessarily be understood from the meanings of its separate parts. When you read an idiom, use the context of the sentence or paragraph to help you identify its meaning. Often, the dictionary will provide an entry that explains how a popular idiom is used.

Example: The salesman needs to sell the last television on the floor. He might sweeten the pot by offering a free three-year warranty.

A. Underline the idiom in each sentence. Write what it means in the space provided. If you have trouble, consult a dictionary.

1. I tried to break the ice by telling the group a story.

_____

2. When I forgot the ending, my older brother said, "That's par for the course. He can never remember a thing."

_____

3. My brother is on the ball. He is always prepared.

_____

4. When I turned in the first draft of my report, the teacher said she wanted to make sure I was on the right track.

_____

5. My mom bends over backwards to get us to our school functions. She sometimes even misses her book-club meetings to take us to ball practice.

_____

B. Write a sentence that contains an idiomatic expression.

6. _____

_____

_____

© Macmillan/McGraw-Hill

At Home: Together, discuss the meaning of this idiom: Did Henry get wind of the weekend plans?

Name _____

You can break words into syllables to help you pronounce them. If you find a word that has a Vowel/Consonant/Consonant/Vowel (**VCCV**) pattern, you should draw a line between the two consonants to break the word into syllables.

Example: Kristi   Kris/ti

Sometimes words will have two sets of VCCV, as in *im/por/tant*.

If you find a word with a Vowel/Consonant/Consonant/Consonant/Vowel (**VCCCV**) pattern, draw the line between one consonant and the digraph or blend of two consonants.

Example: buck/le

Copy the words. Insert lines to break the words when you find VCCV and VCCCV patterns.

1. slipper _____

2. correct _____

3. Cinderella _____

4. matter _____

5. Christmas _____

6. tackle _____

7. children _____

8. pumpkin _____

Choose two words that have the VCCV or the VCCCV pattern. Write them on the lines and draw lines to break them into syllables.

9. _____

10. _____

© Macmillan/McGraw-Hill

At Home: Have the student break the following word into syllables, using the VCCV pattern.

Rumpelstiltskin's Daughter
Grade 6/Unit 2
65

Name _____

Answer each question about a vocabulary word.

outskirts	quarantine	intercept	pedestrians
plight	epidemic	rendezvous	unbearable

1. Where would you be likely to find **pedestrians**? _____

_____

2. Name something that you find **unbearable**. _____

_____

3. What is a synonym for **rendezvous**? _____

_____

4. Where are the **outskirts** of town? _____

_____

5. What kinds of things can you **intercept**? Give two examples. _____

_____

6. If something happens in **epidemic** proportions, how does it happen?

_____

_____

7. Describe in general the **plight** of endangered species. _____

_____

_____

8. When would you need to **quarantine** an animal? _____

_____

_____

© Macmillan/McGraw-Hill

Read the summary of the story "The King of Mazy May" by Jack London.

Walt Masters is the main character of "The King of Mazy May" by Jack London. When Walt was little, his mother died. He and his father moved to the Klondike, a region in Alaska known for its gold. They were prospectors, or people who looked for gold. At the time, prospectors had to make their claims on land quickly or claim jumpers would try to steal the land. Walt, though still a boy, was given the job of protecting his neighbor Loren's claim while Loren traveled on foot to make his claim to the land official.

Walt noticed some strangers who were claim jumpers. He spied on them. He learned that they hoped to get to Dawson to stake the claims before anyone else could. Walt knew he had to do something. He took a team of the claim jumpers' dogs and raced to Dawson. The men followed him closely and actually shot at him. Without the dogs, Walt would have been an easy target. But those dogs saved his life. Not only that, they saved Loren's claim in the end.

Number each event in the order that it happened in the story.

_____ Walt helped Loren save his claim to the land.

_____ Walt and his father moved to the Klondike.

_____ Walt saw some claim jumpers in the area.

_____ Walt's mother died.

_____ Walt took the claim jumpers' dogs and headed for Dawson.

_____ Walt was given the job of protecting his neighbor's claim.

What is your opinion of how Walt acted? On the lines below write a brief paragraph explaining how you feel about what Walt did.

_____

_____

_____

_____

At Home: Together, write a sequence of sentences for a story about a boy who is a hero.

The Great Serum Race
Grade 6/Unit 2
67

© Macmillan/McGraw-Hill

Name _____

As you read *The Great Serum Race,* fill in the Sequence Chart.

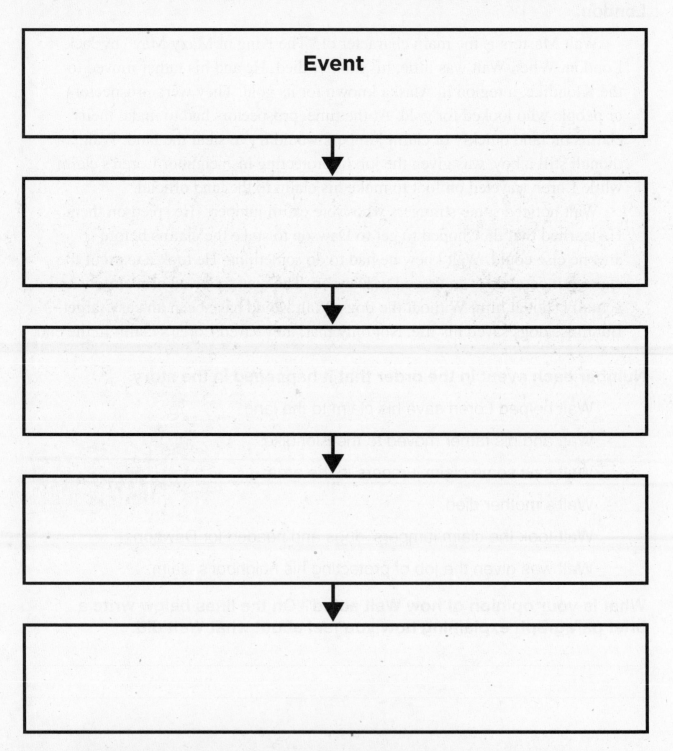

Event

How does the information you wrote in this Sequence Chart help you
monitor comprehension of *The Great Serum Race*?

At Home: Have the student use the chart to retell the story.

© Macmillan/McGraw-Hill

As I read, I will pay attention to the pronunciation of vocabulary and other difficult words.

	On the **outskirts** of Anchorage, Alaska, 12 dogs jump and
9	bark. They have been training for months. Now, these furry
19	athletes and their human driver, or musher, are about to set off on
32	an amazing journey. They're going to race the Iditarod. They'll
42	run more than 1,100 miles up snow-covered mountains, through
50	blizzards, and across frozen tundra and jagged ice sheets.
59	Temperatures may fall to minus 50 degrees Fahrenheit (-45° Celsius).
67	Most animals couldn't hope to survive such dangerous conditions.
76	But these dogs can't wait to begin! They are Alaskan huskies, bred
88	for this weather and this job. They love to run through the icy
101	north.
102	In the late 1800's and early 1900's, many people who lived in
112	Alaska depended on sled dogs. They lived far from transportation.
122	Winters there were harsh. The best way to get around was to use
135	sled dogs. Over the years, the dogs saved many lives. They helped
147	people keep in touch with each other and the outside world.
158	Without the dogs, life might have been **unbearable** for some of
169	the settlers. 171

Comprehension Check

1. What conditions might a sled dog face? **Summarize**

2. What problems did people have in the late 1800's in Alaska? How did dogs help? **Problem and Solution**

	Words Read	−	Number of Errors	=	Words Correct Score
First Read		−		=	
Second Read		−		=	

© Macmillan/McGraw-Hill

At Home: Help the student read the passage, paying attention to the goal at the top of the page.

Haiku is an unrhymed form of Japanese poetry that is usually three lines long.

The first line in Haiku has five syllables; the second line, seven; the third, five. Haiku often describes something in nature.

Symbolism is the use of an everyday object to stand for something more meaningful.

Metaphor is a comparison of two essentially unlike things.

Try your hand at writing haiku. Write three poems that picture different seasons. In at least one poem, include a symbol. For example, flower buds can symbolize the coming of spring. Use a metaphor in at least one poem.

When you finish you may draw a picture for each haiku.

_____

_____

_____

_____

_____

_____

_____

_____

© Macmillan/McGraw-Hill

At Home: Together, write a haiku about objects or scenes from around the house.

Synonyms are words that have the same or nearly the same meaning. You can use synonyms to help you determine the meaning of unfamiliar words. Often, synonyms are used as context clues.

Example: Jennie was scheduled to intercept, or seize, the message at midnight.
The word *seize* is a synonym for *intercept*.

A. Use a dictionary or thesaurus to find a synonym for each of the following words.

1. majestic _____

2. hospitable _____

3. dejected _____

4. abbreviated _____

5. reasonable _____

B. Choose two sets of synonyms from the list above and write a paragraph that includes them.

6. _____

_____

_____

_____

_____

_____

_____

_____

© Macmillan/McGraw-Hill

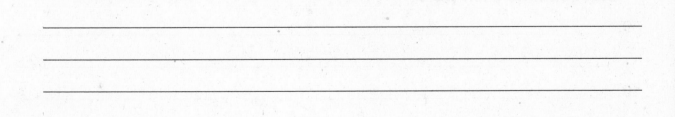

At Home: Together, find as many synonyms for different words as possible.

Recognizing letter patterns in words helps you separate words into syllables.

Vowel-Consonant-Vowel (VCV) patterns can be divided in two different ways.

- If the vowel before the consonant is long, the break comes after the vowel, as in ba/sic. It follows the **V/CV** pattern. It is the most common pattern.
- If the vowel before the consonant is short, the break comes after the consonant, as in rob/in. It follows the **VC/V** pattern.
- If the first syllable is unstressed, as in a/bout, the break comes after the unstressed vowel. It follows the **V/CV** pattern.

You can find where the word should break by sounding out the syllables, using first the long and then the short vowel sounds. The pronunciation that sounds right and the VCV patterns will help you pronounce the word.

A. Copy the words. Draw lines to break the words into syllables when you find a VCV pattern.

1. again _____
2. forest _____
3. student _____
4. desert _____

5. habitat _____
6. Friday _____
7. depict _____
8. delight _____

B. Choose two of the words from the above list. Write one sentence that contains each word.

9. _____
_____

10. _____
_____

© Macmillan/McGraw-Hill

At Home: Help students pronounce new words by looking through written material and identifying VCV patterns.

Use the clues to complete the crossword.

Across

4. an area remote from the center
5. extremely rich and magnificent
6. written on or engraved
7. self-consciousness or shame
8. a restraint upon the activities of people to prevent the spread of disease
10. people walking

Down

1. similarity or likeness
2. figuring by mathematical processes
3. accidental events that seem to be connected
9. not finished

© Macmillan/McGraw-Hill

A. Write each vocabulary word next to its antonym.

| grouchy | unsatisfactory | spicy |
| sheepishly | prospered | unbearable |

1. _____ boldly

2. _____ acceptable

3. _____ tolerable

4. _____ failed

5. _____ happy

6. _____ mild

B. Write four sentences using the following vocabulary words: *calamities, devastating, evacuate, administer*. Write about a natural disaster.

7. _____

_____

8. _____

_____

9. _____

_____

10. _____

_____

© Macmillan/McGraw-Hill

Name _____

A. Fill in each blank with a vocabulary word.

flourish	foreman	employee	fulfill
gleefully	gloated	vigorously	gritted

1. The cowboy _____ his teeth as he clung to the bucking bronco.

2. The man _____ about his special ability to lasso cattle.

3. The children _____ ran home so they could play outside.

4. The team practiced _____ all afternoon, and they were tired when they finished.

5. The new _____ reported directly to the manager of the company.

6. Grapes and oranges _____ in southern California.

7. Many boys hoped to _____ their dreams of becoming cowboys.

8. The _____ of the farm decides which crops will be picked next.

B. Choose two vocabulary words from the list above. Use them in sentences of your own.

9. _____

_____

10. _____

_____

© Macmillan/McGraw-Hill

Read the passage and answer the questions.

Before the American Southwest was American, Spanish and Mexican settlers made their homes in the places we now call Texas, New Mexico, Arizona, and southern California. Many descendants of these early settlers still remain. Ranching was the business to be in, and my relatives were *rancheros* or ranch owners. My name is Hernando Arturo Castillo. When I was a boy, most of my nights were filled with adventure stories told around the campfire. My friends were the *gauchos*, Spanish for cowboys. That's all I ever wanted to be. Their lives seemed so daring, even though the work was hard. I never became a gaucho, partly because I tried it. When I was sixteen, I went with the gauchos on a cattle drive to the Northwest. Saying the work was hard was an understatement! I have never been so tired and scared as I was on those lonely plains at night. From that point on, I knew I would do better as a *ranchero*. I followed in my father's footsteps, much to his delight.

1. Where is the passage set? Why is the setting important?

_____

_____

_____

_____

_____

2. Who is the main character in the passage? Describe his perspective as he narrates his own story.

_____

_____

_____

_____

_____

© Macmillan/McGraw-Hill

At Home: Together read a short story and discuss character, setting, and plot.

Name _____

As you read *Juan Verdades,* fill in the Character, Setting, Plot Chart

Characters	Setting	Plot

How does the information you wrote in this Character, Setting, Plot Chart
help you monitor comprehension of *Juan Verdades*?

At Home: Have the students use the chart to retell the story.

© Macmillan/McGraw-Hill

As I read, I will pay attention to pauses, stops, and intonation.

	If Benny Stone could see what lay ahead, he'd probably
10	be itching to get to Old Mesilla. Instead, he squirmed. The
21	car seat was hot and made him sweat more. His neck itched
33	and he wished he were back home.
40	His mom, however, was a different story. The farther they
50	got from Minneapolis, the lighter Benny's mother seemed.
58	It was as if she was shedding burdens onto the highway as
70	they traveled southwest, the convertible top pulled back.
78	Suddenly, she jabbed her finger at the windshield. "Look!
87	There it is!" In the backseat, Garcia, Benny's black Labrador
97	retriever, turned obediently, whipping himself in the face
105	with one wind-blown ear.
109	A large sign loomed on the side of the road. "Welcome
120	to New Mexico, the Land of Enchantment," Benny read
129	as it zoomed out of view. He had stopped complaining.
139	Seeing his mom all grinning and light was almost worth the
150	trip. Well, almost. He could still name about ten things he'd
161	rather do this summer than spend it with his mother in some
173	tiny southwestern town. 176

Comprehension Check

1. Why does Benny change his mind about New Mexico? **Character, Setting, Plot**

2. How do you think Benny's summer is going to turn out? **Make Predictions**

	Words Read	–	Number of Errors	=	Words Correct Score
First Read		–		=	
Second Read		–		=	

© Macmillan/McGraw-Hill

At Home: Help the student read the passage, paying attention to the goal at the top of the page.

Name _____

> **Maps** are used to show the features of an area. A map usually
> has a compass rose to show you north/south orientation. A map
> also has a scale to show the relationship between the distances
> on the map and the actual distances between physical locations.

**The map below shows some unusual place names in the western
United States.**

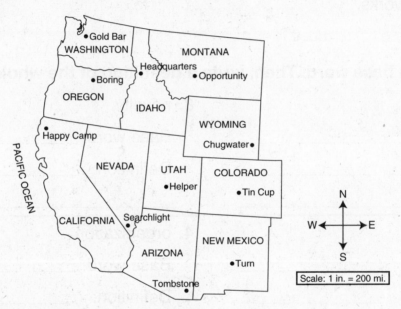

Use the map to answer the questions.

1. What does the map show?

   _____

   _____

2. In which state is Searchlight found? _____

3. Which city on the map is located in Montana? _____

4. Which state is north of Boring, Oregon? _____

5. Which city is about 400 miles west of Chugwater, Wyoming?

   _____

© Macmillan/McGraw-Hill

At Home: Together, use a road map to figure out directions
from one place to another.

Words consist of a variety of parts: prefixes, base words, suffixes, and inflectional endings. **Base words** give the heart of a word's meaning. If you can identify and understand the base word, you can use your knowledge of its meaning to determine the meaning of a larger word.

Example: I hope to find a qualified <u>employee</u>.

The base of the word *employee* is *employ*, which means "use or work." The suffix *-ee* means "one who." Therefore, the word *employee* means "one who works."

A. Write each base word. Then, write a definition of the whole word.

1. illness

Base word: _____

Definition: _____

_____

2. memorial

Base word: _____

Definition: _____

_____

3. novelty

Base word: _____

Definition: _____

_____

4. organization

Base word: _____

Definition: _____

_____

B. Choose two words from above. Use them in sentences of your own.

5. _____

_____

6. _____

_____

© Macmillan/McGraw-Hill

At Home: Have the student identify any unfamiliar words in a newspaper article by applying what he or she knows about its parts.

Name _____

When you read words with two or more syllables, you will find that at least one of the syllables is accented. Say the word *wagon*. The accented sound in that word is *wa*. Some words have the accent at the other end of the word. Say *again*. This time *gain* is accented. The schwa sound is never accented.

A. Say each word aloud and write each word on the line provided. Divide each word in syllables. Place a stressmark in front of the accented syllable.

1. flourish _____

2. remind _____

3. mixture _____

4. about _____

5. mobile _____

6. tennis _____

7. delight _____

8. fiber _____

9. promote _____

10. trial _____

B. Choose two of the words from the list and use each in a sentence.

11. _____

_____

12. _____

_____

At Home: Together, come up with a list of words with two syllables and decide where the accent is in each word.

Juan Verdades • **Grade 6/Unit 3**   81

© Macmillan/McGraw-Hill

Name _____

A. Write each vocabulary word next to its definition.

embarked	promenade	unimaginable	sensational
extravagant	lamented	precarious	limousine

1. expressed regret _____

2. not thinkable _____

3. leisurely walk _____

4. started out _____

5. arousing an intense interest _____

6. characterized by a lack of stability _____

7. large, luxurious automobile _____

8. extremely elaborate _____

B. Choose two vocabulary words. Use them in sentences of your own. Then draw a picture in the box below to illustrate one of your sentences.

9. _____

_____

10. _____

_____

© Macmillan/McGraw-Hill

Read the passage and answer the questions.

"Joshua, are you writing again?" asked Mrs. Talbot for what seemed like the hundredth time. "If you don't come down and participate in life, you aren't going to have anything to write about!"

Joshua didn't agree. He spent lots of time living. But he also spent lots of time writing. He recorded what happened during the school day, during breakfast, during dinner, and during playtime with friends. But in his writing, all the things happened on Mars set hundreds of years before or after they actually happened. It seemed to him that his life was much more interesting when he put it somewhere else in time or space. After all, Joshua planned on being a writer when he grew up. He needed lots of practice.

1. How does Joshua's mother feel about his writing?

   _____

2. What kind of writing does Joshua do? _____

   _____

   _____

   _____

3. Why does Joshua write stories about everything that happens to him?

   _____

4. How does Joshua feel about his life? _____

   _____

   _____

Write a short paragraph about your life as if it were set in another place and time. Use another sheet of paper if you need to.

   _____

   _____

   _____

   _____

© Macmillan/McGraw-Hill

At Home: Together read a short story and share some conclusions you draw from your reading.

Nothing Ever Happens on
90th Street • Grade 6/Unit 3

83

Name _____

As you read *Nothing Ever Happens on 90th Street,* fill in the
Conclusions Chart.

What I Know	Text Evidence	Conclusions

How does the information you wrote in this Conclusions Chart help you
monitor comprehension of *Nothing Ever Happens on 90th Street*?

At Home: Have the student use the chart to retell the story.

© Macmillan/McGraw-Hill

As I read, I will pay attention to punctuation.

	September 15, 3:41 P.M.
2	Hello, Peter Smith of Portland, Oregon. This is Julie Taylor
12	of Monterey, California. You may wonder why I'm writing
21	to you, since we don't know each other. It's because my entire
33	class is abuzz. Everybody is talking about Mr. Mora's big
43	announcement today. Mr. Mora is my teacher. Well, not just
53	mine, of course, but he's the teacher for our whole class.
64	My school is called Old Monterey Middle School, which is
74	a boring name. I would have called it the Monterey School
85	for Future Writers and Other Geniuses.
91	Mr. Mora laughed when I told him that. He said, "Well,
102	Julie, that name is a bit long, don't you agree?"
112	Mr. Mora is always asking us if we agree. Most of the
124	time I do. Mr. Mora knows a lot, especially about writing—
135	which brings me to the exciting announcement.
142	"Settle down, please," said Mr. Mora. It was almost three
152	o'clock, and we were getting restless. "I'm going to give you
163	a homework assignment—with a twist." 169

Comprehension Check

1. How do you think Peter Smith will respond? **Draw Conclusions**

2. How can you tell that Julie is a creative thinker? **Make Inferences**

	Words Read	–	Number of Errors	=	Words Correct Score
First Read		–		=	
Second Read		–		=	

© Macmillan/McGraw-Hill

At Home: Help the student read the passage, paying attention to the goal at the top of the page.

Nothing Ever Happens on 90ᵗʰ Street • **Grade 6/Unit 3**

85

When you interview a person, your purpose is to get specific information from her or him. Use the following guidelines for interviewing:

- Write your questions before the interview. Be sure to avoid questions that can be answered with a *yes* or a *no* answer.
- At the beginning of the interview, state your purpose directly.
- Remember that your job is to listen, not talk, during the interview.
- Listen closely to the responses, taking brief notes. If possible, tape-record the interview so you can revisit the information later. Be sure to get permission to tape.
- Ask follow-up questions to get more information or clarification about a topic.
- Immediately after the interview, review your notes and add information so you don't forget it later.

Suppose that you are preparing to interview your favorite author. You can focus the interview on his or her life, profession, a specific book, or another issue. Write a clear statement of your purpose. Then write five questions that will help you gather that information.

Purpose: _____

_____

1. _____

2. _____

_____

3. _____

_____

4. _____

_____

5. _____

_____

© Macmillan/McGraw-Hill

At Home: Take turns writing questions and then interviewing each other.

Name _____

> Dictionaries provide readers with the histories of words as well as their meanings. The word's **origin** usually follows the pronunciation key and the identification of it as a part of speech. If you don't understand the abbreviations in the entry, check the front of the dictionary for a guide to the abbreviations. Some common ones are ME for Middle English, OE for Old English, F for French, L for Latin, and Gk for Greek.
>
> Example: **describe** (di skrīb´) *vt* **described**; **describing** [ME, from L *describere*, from *de-* + *scribere* to write] 1. to give an account in words

A. Use a dictionary to find the origins of the words below. Record the earliest origin listed in the dictionary.

1. wrong: _____

2. scissors: _____

3. health: _____

4. govern: _____

5. split: _____

B. Use each of the words above in a sentence.

6. _____

_____

7. _____

_____

8. _____

_____

9. _____

_____

10. _____

_____

© Macmillan/McGraw-Hill

At Home: Together, use the five words in different sentences.

The **final /ər/** sound is a very common sound in the English language. Every vowel can stand for the /ə/sound. It sounds like the beginning *a* in *about;* the *u* in *minute;* the last *e* in *teacher.* In fact, when you see an *-ar* or *-er* at the end of a word, it stands for the final **/ər/** sound. Often, *-or* does the same.

A. Read the sentences. Write the words that have the final /ər/ sound on the line.

1. A writer needs time to think of good subjects. _____

2. Stories are often similar to real life. _____

3. An author can be seen as a messenger. _____

4. He or she teaches lessons through specific subject matter.

   _____

5. Sometimes writing is turned into a show for the television viewer.

   _____

6. Directors, producers, and actors all play a part in bringing us

   entertainment. _____

7. They also deliver messages to the audience. _____

8. Creators of stories play an important role in society. _____

B. Choose two of the words that have the /ər/ sound and use each in a sentence.

9. _____

   _____

10. _____

    _____

At Home: Underline all the words in a newspaper article that have the /ər/ sound.

© Macmillan/McGraw-Hill

A. Answer the questions about the vocabulary words.

1. What is the difference between a *renewable* and a *nonrenewable* resource? Give examples of each. _____

   _____

   _____

2. Name one *adverse* effect that has happened in our environment. _____

   _____

   _____

3. What does it mean to *generate* electricity? _____

   _____

4. What is an *apparatus?* Give an example. _____

   _____

   _____

B. Write a paragraph about using resources responsibly. Use three of the five vocabulary words: *renewable, nonrenewable, adverse, generate, apparatus.* **Underline the vocabulary words you use.**

_____

_____

_____

_____

_____

_____

_____

_____

© Macmillan/McGraw-Hill

Read the paragraph. Then answer the questions.

"Building Green" is one way to conserve natural resources and protect the environment, but it is expensive and requires dedication to change. There are other ways you can conserve energy that will result in reduced pollution, and you don't have to move! One way to conserve energy is to pay attention to the heating and cooling in your home. If you turn the thermostat down in the winter and up in the summer, the result is a significant decrease in the use of electricity or gas. Even changing the temperature a few degrees will save a bundle of energy. Another way to conserve natural resources is to put the car keys away. Cars use gasoline, which comes from a nonrenewable resource. If you can, take a bus or train, ride a bike, or walk. Doing so will help you save money on gasoline, reduce the amount of fossil fuels you use, and help the environment by not burning those fuels. Going green is easier than you think!

1. What is the effect of turning down the heat in the winter?

_____

2. How can you help the environment? _____

_____

_____

3. Name three effects of not driving.

A. _____

B. _____

C. _____

4. Why is "going green" easy to do? _____

_____

_____

_____

© Macmillan/McGraw-Hill

At Home: Together, discuss ways that you can work together to help the planet.

As you read *Building Green,* fill in the Cause and Effect Chart.

Cause	→	Effect
	→	
	→	
	→	

How does the information you wrote in this Cause and Effect Chart help you monitor comprehension of *Building Green*?

© Macmillan/McGraw-Hill

At Home: Have the students use the chart to retell the story.

As I read, I will pay attention to intonation and pausing.

	Click on the TV. Turn up the heat. Go for a ride in the car.
15	What do all these actions have in common? They all use
26	energy. Energy is an important part of our lives. Try to
37	imagine going through a day without it. First take away
47	everything that uses electricity. No refrigerator, no TV, no
56	light bulbs. Then shut down everything that runs on gasoline
66	or fuel. No cars, trucks, planes, or trains. Next turn off the
78	natural gas or oil that keeps your home warm on bitter cold
90	nights. You get the idea—energy powers our lives.
99	Most of the energy we use comes from fossil fuels—coal,
110	oil, and natural gas. These energy sources are called fossil
120	fuels because they formed from plants and animals that died
130	millions of years ago.
134	Fossil fuels have many uses. Power plants burn coal and
144	oil to generate electricity. Gasoline and fuel for most cars,
154	planes, trains, and ships come from oil. Oil and natural gas
165	provide heat for homes. In many ways, fossil fuels are
175	excellent sources of energy. 179

Comprehension Check

1. What is the main idea of this passage? **Main Idea and Details**

2. What would happen if electricity were taken away? **Draw Conclusions**

	Words Read	–	Number of Errors	=	Words Correct Score
First Read		–		=	
Second Read		–		=	

© Macmillan/McGraw-Hill

At Home: Help the student read the passage, paying attention to the goal at the top of the page.

Study Strategies are ways that help you learn new material and manage the information you already know.

Skimming—Look over material you have read. Don't read every word. Just look at the headings, boldfaced words, italicized sentences, pictures, and other things that stand out in the text. What do you know about them?

Scanning—If you need specific information about the Revolutionary War, for example, scan the text for key words that relate to the subject. Make a note of pictures, time lines, or other visuals that might have something to do with the topic you are reviewing.

Notetaking—If you haven't already done so, take notes on the most important aspects of the text. Record important terms and dates. Write brief definitions or descriptions to remind you of the knowledge you already have.

Outlining—One way to clearly identify main points is to construct outlines of sections of text. You can use a formal or informal outline. Whatever you choose, be sure to record the main ideas and supporting details in the text.

Choose a chapter or section from your social studies or science book. Skim the text for the most important information. Make an outline of the reading in the space below.

_____

_____

_____

_____

_____

_____

_____

_____

© Macmillan/McGraw-Hill

At Home: Together, create a space for study, possibly at a desk or a table.

Building Green • **Grade 6/Unit 3**   93

Practice

Name _____

Vocabulary Strategy:
Context Clues Within a
Sentence

Context refers to the words and sentences that surround an unfamiliar word. **Context clues** come in different forms but are often included **within the same sentence** as the unfamiliar word. Sometimes the clues will be in the form of definitions, restatements, or synonyms. Other times, the clue will be in a contrasting word. Often the general context will give you an idea about the meaning of the word.

Use the context clues in the sentences to define the underlined words.

1. We need to be <u>economical</u>, not wasteful, with natural resources.

   _____

2. Mining for natural resources often destroys the <u>habitats</u>, or homes, of endangered animals.

   _____

3. If we use fewer <u>fossil fuels</u>, such as oil and coal, that are made from the remains of plants and animals, there will be less demand for them.

   _____

4. If more <u>efficient</u> cars are built, they will use less gasoline and oil to run, and will place less stress on the environment.

   _____

5. <u>Architects</u>, the people who design buildings, are coming up with new ways to save energy every day.

   _____

6. To <u>purify</u>, or clean the air, people should plant more trees.

   _____

© Macmillan/McGraw-Hill

At Home: Together, read a story to determine the meaning of unfamiliar words by using the surrounding context clues.

The **final /ən/** sound can be represented by an *-on* or an *-en*. This sound is always in an unaccented syllable, as in *weapon* and *frighten*.
The **final /əl/** sound can be spelled as *-le, -al,* and *-el,* as in *struggle, mental,* and *channel*. This syllable is also unaccented.

A. Fill in the correct letters to make the final /ən/ sound in the following words.

1. wag _____

2. deep _____

3. op _____

B. Fill in the correct letters to make the final /əl/ sound in the following words.

4. dent _____

5. doub _____

6. flann _____

C. Circle the words that follow the spelling patterns that stand for the final /ən/ and /əl/ sounds.

7. The solar panel will help heat the house.

8. The wind tunnel provides energy to make electricity.

9. I love to go to street fairs and eat funnel cake.

10. My brother loves to frighten me and he is very good at it.

© Macmillan/McGraw-Hill

At Home: Together, play a word challenge game. Each player should come up with a word that has one of the /ə/ sounds discussed here.

Building Green • Grade 6/Unit 3   95

Name _____

Complete the crossword using the vocabulary words.

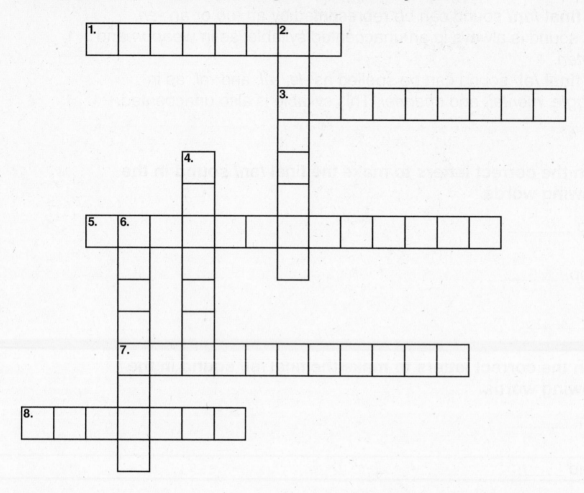

Across

1. ditches used as a military defense

3. highly ordered stage of cultural development

5. having a belief in chance

7. firmly

8. to lengthen in time

Down

2. dig up

4. to come before

6. useful tools or implements often for kitchen use

© Macmillan/McGraw-Hill

Name _____

Write a summary of the paragraph on the lines provided. Be sure to state the main ideas in your own words.

An archaeologist is a person who studies the cultural and physical remains of past civilizations. Some archaeologists study bones. Others study artifacts, which are things from ancient civilizations like artwork, tools, and buildings. Archaeologists can have many different specialties. Sometimes they spend time researching the past. Many archaeologists spend time doing fieldwork—collecting and observing information while digging at a site. And, maybe most importantly, they have to put all the things they find together to form theories about the past, whether it is a particular civilization or animal. Certain evidence provides information about the way people and animals lived and behaved. For example, the way an animal's teeth are formed might indicate what kind of food the animal ate. By putting this information together, archaeologists can give us theories of how people lived thousands of years ago.

_____

_____

_____

_____

_____

_____

_____

_____

_____

_____

_____

_____

© Macmillan/McGraw-Hill

At Home: Find a short nonfiction article. Then write a summary of it.

Name _____

As you read *The Emperor's Silent Army*, fill in the Summary Chart.

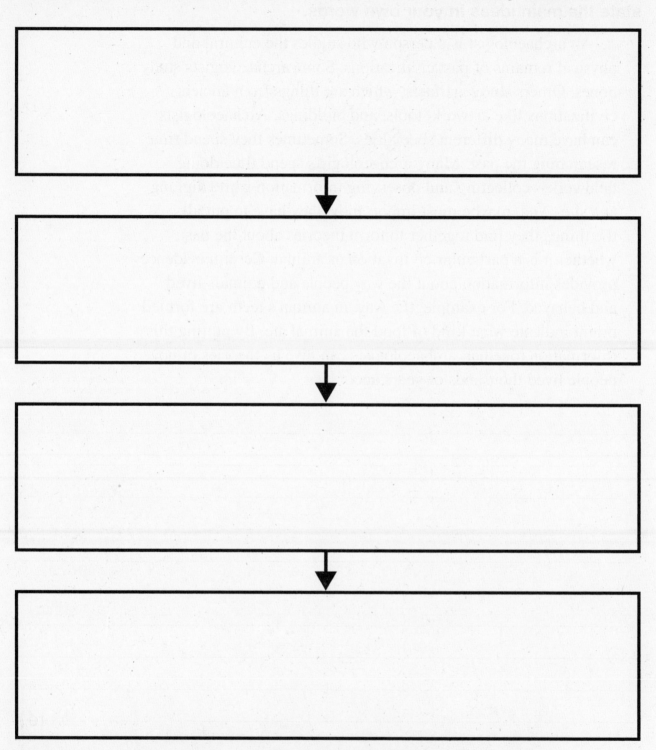

How does the information you wrote in this Summary Chart help you
monitor comprehension of *The Emperor's Silent Army*?

At Home: Have the student use the chart to retell the story.

© Macmillan/McGraw-Hill

Name _____

As I read, I will pay attention to tempo.

	Archaeologists discovered the first examples of cave art in
9	the early 1800s. In Europe alone Stone Age art appears in
19	hundreds of places. Most are found on rocks. At first, some
30	scientists had doubts about the age of this art. They didn't think
42	that Paleolithic people could have invented a way to make light
53	that would allow them to work in pitch-black caves.
62	Then, around 1900, an archaeologist found a decorated
69	piece of sandstone. It had once been used to burn animal fat,
81	creating light. It must have been used as a lamp. This was the
94	first prehistoric lamp ever found.
99	Early in the 1960s, another French scientist discovered a
107	similar lamp in the Lascaux cave. Scientists now agree that
117	ancient artists must have used fat-burning lamps while they
126	worked inside the caves.
130	Many of the paintings at Lascaux are high on the walls and
142	ceiling. How were the artists able to reach such out-of-the-way
152	places? Evenly spaced holes found along the walls are a clue.
163	They suggest that the artists built wooden scaffolds, or
172	platforms, to stand on while they worked. 179

Comprehension Check

1. How did the Paleolithic people paint caves in the pitch dark? **Summarize**

2. Why did archaeologists at first doubt that the cave art was from Paleolithic people? **Draw Conclusions**

	Words Read	–	Number of Errors	=	Words Correct Score
First Read		–		=	
Second Read		–		=	

© Macmillan/McGraw-Hill

At Home: Help the student read the passage, paying attention to the goal at the top of the page.

Name _____

> **Meter** is the rhythmical pattern of unstressed and stressed syllables in a line of poetry. Iambic pentameter, or five pairs of short-long syllables, is the most common meter.
>
> **Consonance** is the repetition of consonant sounds at the beginning or ends of two or more words grouped together. For example, *creak* and *crock*.

Mark the meter of the first three lines of "Ozymandias." Underline the stressed syllables.

I met a traveler from an antique land

Who said: Two vast and trunkless legs of stone

Stand in the desert . . .

Circle the words that show consonance in the following lines.

Clip-clop went the horse's hooves

As she trotted across the park to be patted on the head.

Now write a short poem of your own. Use consonance in your poem.

_____

_____

_____

_____

_____

_____

_____

_____

_____

© Macmillan/McGraw-Hill

At Home: Read a poem aloud. Work together to mark the meter of the poem.

Words can consist of a variety of parts: prefixes, base words, suffixes, and inflectional endings. **Prefixes** are attached to the beginnings of words and often change the words' meanings.

Look at the following chart of prefixes and their meanings.

Prefix	Meaning	Example
un- il- dis-	not, without, the opposite of	unhappy illegal disappear
re-	do again	retype
super- extra-	beyond or above	superhuman extraordinary
anti-	against	antibiotics anti-inflammatory
bi-	two	bicycle

A. Write the meaning of each word. Use your knowledge of prefixes to help you define the words.

1. bisect: _____

2. reclassify: _____

3. unloved: _____

4. disapprove: _____

5. illiterate: _____

B. Think of three words that use the prefixes in the chart. Use a dictionary to check whether the word can take the prefix.

6. _____

7. _____

8. _____

 At Home: Give the student a list of common words and help him or her build new words by adding prefixes.

© Macmillan/McGraw-Hill

Name _____

A **prefix** is a syllable that comes at the beginning of a word. It usually changes the meaning of the base word or the root.

If you do not know what the prefix of a word means, try to think of another word with **the same prefix.** You may not know what supergravity is, but you probably know what a superhero is. You can apply the meaning of *super (over and above, larger)* to the new word.

A. Underline each prefix in the words below. Write a meaning for the prefix.

1. provide _____

2. review _____

3. tricycle _____

4. illegal _____

5. ungrateful _____

6. disgrace _____

B. Use four of the words above in sentences of your own.

7. _____

_____

8. _____

_____

9. _____

_____

10. _____

_____

At Home: Write a list of other words that have prefixes and find their meanings.

© Macmillan/McGraw-Hill

Name _____

Write the vocabulary word next to its synonym.

sponsoring	array	significance	charismatic
mimics	despondently	sleuthing	anonymous

1. importance _____

2. searching _____

3. imitates _____

4. hopelessly _____

5. attractive _____

6. supporting _____

7. group _____

8. unknown _____

Choose four vocabulary words and write a sentence for each. Underline the vocabulary words you use in your sentences.

9. _____
   _____

10. _____
   _____

11. _____
   _____

12. _____
   _____

© Macmillan/McGraw-Hill

Read the passage and answer the questions.

"I can't go out there," Sam said, as she peeked through the stage curtains at the ever-growing audience. "I just can't do it!" She was nearly in tears.

"Honey, you will be fantastic, really," Mrs. Mosley, Sam's drama teacher said. "Besides, if you don't go out there, we won't have a show! You are the star, after all."

Over the last six weeks, Sam had practiced and practiced and practiced her lines. She knew them forward and backward. But they had all left her mind the minute she saw the audience—the huge crowd that would be looking right at her!

"Curtain time!" said Mrs. Mosley.

Sam, despite her knocking knees and quivering voice, walked out onstage and delivered her first line. By the time she finished her first scene, she had forgotten there even was an audience. She was a hit!

1. How does Sam feel at the beginning? _____

_____

2. What information supports this conclusion? _____

_____

3. How well is Sam prepared for the performance? Support your conclusions.

_____

_____

4. How do Sam's feelings change? Support your conclusion.

_____

_____

5. Do you think Sam will continue to act? Support your conclusion.

_____

_____

© Macmillan/McGraw-Hill

At Home: Extend the story by making up something that happens right after the play, involving Sam and the audience.

As you read *The Case of the Phantom Poet,* fill in the
Conclusions Chart.

Text Clues	Conclusion

How does the information you wrote in this Conclusions Chart help you
monitor comprehension of *The Case of the Phantom Poet*?

 At Home: Have the student use the chart to retell the story.

© Macmillan/McGraw-Hill

As I read, I will pay attention to dialogue, tempo, and intonation.

9	*(The stage in the school auditorium; Erica reads aloud*
19	*from a script. Joel practices karate. They are unaware that*
23	*Jesse is watching them.)*
	Erica: "Ranger: Old Teddy's going to hurt somebody soon."
32	Joel, say that line **despondently** so the audience sees how
42	upset you are. Should I write *unhappily* in the stage direction
53	instead of *despondently*?
56	**Joel:** I'm feeling despondent about this play. There's not
65	enough action in it. I should be a karate instructor instead of
77	a park ranger.
80	**Erica:** It's set in a forest. It's about a bear that gets into
93	campers' stuff. It's about how people have to learn to respect
104	animals' homes.
106	**Joel:** I could be a ranger who teaches karate in his spare time.
119	*(He chops the air and kicks one leg to the side.)* Pow! Take
132	that, Old Teddy! Erica, I'm going to make up my own lines.
144	**Erica:** You're going to ruin my play!
151	**Joel:** You're going to ruin my acting career!
159	**Erica:** A real actor follows the script and listens to what the
171	director tells him. 174

Comprehension Check

1. How would you summarize what the play is about? **Summarize**

2. How do you think this conflict between Joel and Erica will end? **Make Predictions**

	Words Read	–	Number of Errors	=	Words Correct Score
First Read		–		=	
Second Read		–		=	

© Macmillan/McGraw-Hill

106 The Case of the Phantom Poet
Grade 6/Unit 3

At Home: Help the student read the passage, paying attention to the goal at the top of the page.

Tables are used to organize information so that it is easily accessible. Columns help you organize the information into different categories. Rows helps you repeat similar information.

Here is some information about some Broadway shows. *Bingo* is playing at the Starstruck. It has its first preview on December 7 and opens on January 24. *Class Zoo* is opening on March 15 at the Kids' Stage. *Class Zoo* has its first preview on February 12. *Caesar* opens at the Tall Theater in previews on March 8. *Caesar* then opens on April 3. *Western* has previews on March 26. It opens April 26 at Studio 50. The Ford Center has previews of *Iceberg* on March 29. *Iceberg* opens on April 28.

Make a table with four columns. Title your columns Play, Theater, Preview and Opening. Fill in the table with the appropriate information. Then use it to answer the questions.

1. How many shows are listed? _____

2. Which play is opening on April 3? _____

3. When is the first preview of *Class Zoo*? _____

4. Where is *Iceberg* being staged? _____

5. Which play is being performed at the Starstruck? _____

6. If you were visiting New York from March 25 to April 7, which previews could you attend? _____

© Macmillan/McGraw-Hill

At Home: Use a table or chart to plan a trip and find information, such as the shortest trip, the most expensive trip, or the last train.

Using analogies requires you to understand how words relate to each other. Analogies are written like this: happy : joyful :: significance : importance. They are read like this: *happy* is to *joyful* as *significance* is to *importance*. **Synonyms,** words that mean the same or nearly the same thing, are often used in analogies, as in the example.

A. Choose the best word to complete the following analogies.
   Circle the letter of the correct answer.

1. jumped : leaped :: laughed :

   a. cried   **c.** chuckled

   b. hoped   **d.** smiled

2. close : shut :: perform :

   a. forget   **c.** imitate

   b. act   **d.** quiet

3. child : kid :: drama :

   a. play   **c.** violence

   b. tragic   **d.** comic

4. dinner : supper :: academy :

   a. breakfast   **c.** obey

   b. title   **d.** school

5. friend : pal :: author :

   a. writer   **c.** lead

   b. character   **d.** actor

B. Write an analogy of your own that uses synonyms.

6. _____

© Macmillan/McGraw-Hill

The Case of the Phantom Poet
Grade 6/Unit 3

At Home: Together, create three analogies. Make sure that the analogies are synonyms.

You can change a base word that is a verb to a noun by **adding** some form of the *-ion, -ation* ending. For example to change the verb *navigate* to a noun, drop the last e and add *-ion*: navigation.

Sometimes because of the way the word sounds you have to use the alternative ending *-ation,* as in *commendation.*

A good test for which ending to use would be to see if you can pronounce the word with the *-ion* ending. *Commendion* is very hard to say, so we use the *-ation* ending for *commendation.*

A. Read each verb below and decide which ending you should use to change it to a noun. Try out the *-ion* ending first. If that does not sound correct, then use *-ation*. Write your nouns on the lines that follow each base word.

1. consider _____

2. decorate _____

3. promote _____

4. act _____

5. confess _____

6. satisfy _____

7. confuse _____

8. express _____

Use four of the nouns in sentences of your own.

9. _____

10. _____

11. _____

12. _____

At Home: Together, find three words that follow the *-ion, -ation* patterns in a story that the student chooses.

The Case of the Phantom Poet
Grade 6/Unit 3   109

© Macmillan/McGraw-Hill

Name _____

A. Write each vocabulary word next to its synonym.

vigorously	gleefully	unimaginable	extravagant
generate	adverse	prolong	significance

1. make _____

2. importance _____

3. bad _____

4. luxurious _____

5. extend _____

6. joyfully _____

7. powerfully _____

8. incredible _____

B. Write the vocabulary word from the box that is a context clue for the underlined words.

nonrenewable	utensils	gritted	sleuthing

9. My <u>detective work</u> and _____ skills were well known.

10. <u>Disposable</u> cameras are _____.

11. Jessica <u>ground</u> and _____ her teeth before her parachute jump.

12. Jason preferred <u>chopsticks</u> to other eating _____.

© Macmillan/McGraw-Hill

Name _____

A. Complete each sentence with one or more vocabulary words.

> gloated   fulfill   sensational   precarious   superstitious
> precede   steadfastly   array   anonymous   charismatic

1. The _____ speaker told _____ stories that held the audience's attention.

2. My _____ aunt warned me not to walk under a ladder.

3. As the cat looked down from the top of the tree, he realized just how _____ his position was.

4. I wanted to read more by this author, but she is _____.

5. Someday I will _____ my dream of becoming a filmmaker.

6. The appetizers _____ the main course at dinner.

7. The doctor gazed _____ upon the wide _____ of different surgical instruments.

8. Even though Jo was taught to be a gracious winner, she secretly _____ when she beat the boastful boy.

B. Choose two vocabulary words and use each of them in a sentence.

9. _____

   _____

10. _____

   _____

© Macmillan/McGraw-Hill

A. Write the vocabulary word that best matches each clue.

> summit   awesome   specialists   deteriorated
> maturity   guidance   peripheral   typical

1. this is what you need when you are lost _____

2. this is what you show when you act like a grown-up _____

3. these kinds of doctors only work in one area of medicine; neurosurgeons
   are examples of _____

4. you might use this word to describe something that causes wonder
   _____

5. if you reach the top of the mountain, you are standing on this
   _____

6. you might use this word to describe something ordinary
   _____

7. you use this kind of vision to see things out the corner of your eye
   _____

8. if something has gotten worse it has done this _____

B. Write two sentences using four vocabulary words from above. Underline the words you use.

9. _____

   _____

10. _____

    _____

© Macmillan/McGraw-Hill

Remember that authors usually have one of three main **purposes** for writing: to inform, to persuade, or to entertain. To accomplish their purpose, authors choose their words very carefully. They want to clearly express their attitudes and ideas about certain topics.

A. Read each passage and then write what you think was the author's primary purpose for writing.

1. John Muir was one of North America's greatest conservationists. He worked steadfastly to persuade the United States government to protect such wilderness preserves as Yosemite. He also helped establish the Sierra Club in 1892.

   Author's purpose: _____

   _____

2. Once upon a time in a village in China, an extraordinary young woman was born. At that time girls were not considered good luck. She proved this belief wrong when she grew up to be the hero who saved her village.

   Author's purpose: _____

   _____

3. Remember that heroes come in all shapes and sizes. Most importantly, you too can be an uncommon hero! All you need to do is to donate to our cause. Your help will make you a hero in everyone's eyes.

   Author's purpose: _____

   _____

B. Choose one of the stated purposes for writing and rewrite one of the passages above as if the author had a different purpose for writing. Use the lines below to rewrite your passage.

4. _____

   _____

   _____

At Home: Discuss an article or a broadcast and decide what the author's purpose is.

Seeing Things His Own Way
Grade 6/Unit 4

113

© Macmillan/McGraw-Hill

Name _____

**As you read "Seeing Things His Own Way," fill in the Author's
Purpose Chart.**

Clues	Author's Purpose

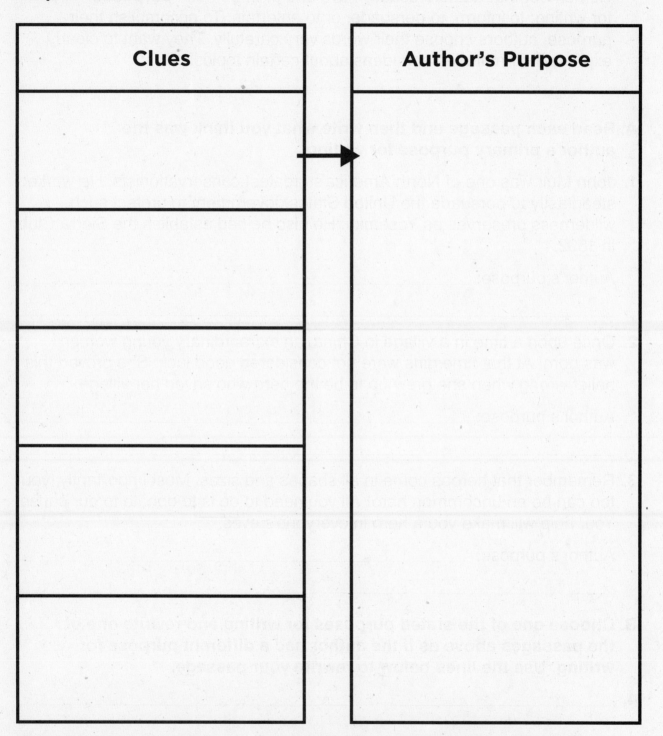

How does the information you wrote in this Author's Purpose Chart help
you monitor comprehension of "Seeing Things His Own Way"?

At Home: Have the student use the chart to retell the story.

© Macmillan/McGraw-Hill

As I read, I will pay attention to pauses, stops, and intonation.

	Marla Runyan is a competitive Olympic athlete. She is
9	also legally blind. Though you might guess that Marla is
19	very different from other athletes, in most ways, she really
29	isn't. She has had injuries and disappointments. She has had
39	victories, too. She has changed coaches and tried new events.
49	She has been good at a lot of things, and awesome at a few.
63	She is stubborn, competitive, and proud.
69	What does make Marla different is that she lacks full
79	vision. She has only **peripheral** vision. This means she can
89	see only the outer edges of what most people normally view.
100	For example, if she looks at a picture of a person, she
112	might see only the top of his head, his fingertips, and his
124	shoes. The rest of his body is a blur of colors.
135	Marla's vision problems are uncommon in the world of
144	top-notch athletes, but what really makes her different is that
154	she hasn't let poor vision stop her from doing what she loves
166	and doing her best. 170

Comprehension Check

1. How would you summarize Marla's athletic career? **Summarize**

2. What does the author want you to know about Marla? **Author's Purpose**

	Words Read	–	Number of Errors	=	Words Correct Score
First Read		–		=	
Second Read		–		=	

© Macmillan/McGraw-Hill

At Home: Help the student read the passage, paying attention to the goal at the top of the page.

Seeing Things His Own Way
Grade 6/Unit 4   115

Diagrams are visual illustrations that show you how something is put together or arranged. When you look at a diagram, make sure you read all the **labels** so you can be clear about what is presented. Tables are used to organize information to make it easily accessible.

Use the diagram to answer the questions.

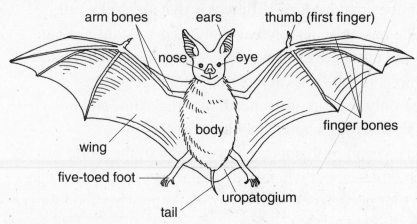

Bat Anatomy

1. What does the diagram show? _____

2. What is the uropatagium? _____

_____

3. Where are a bat's thumbs located? _____

4. How many fingers do bats have? _____

5. How many toes does a bat have? _____

6. Use the lines below to write a paragraph about bats. Use what you already knew about bats and what you might have learned from the diagram.

_____

_____

_____

© Macmillan/McGraw-Hill

At Home: Together, discuss some instructions that include a diagram and labels.

When you encounter an unfamiliar word, check the context within which it is used. One kind of context clue is a **synonym** of the word used in the same passage, often within the same sentence.

Example: The biker relied on her <u>peripheral</u>, or <u>side</u>, vision as she changed lanes.
The words *peripheral* and *side* are synonyms.

Fill in the blank in each sentence with a synonym of the underlined word.

1. Rachel found mangoes so <u>delicious</u> and _____ that they have replaced strawberries as her favorite fruit.

2. Madison wanted to learn how to ski, but she didn't want to pay for a ski <u>instructor</u>, so she decided to read a book and become her own _____.

3. José rode his bike in the city, but when the first bus <u>rushed</u> past him and then another car _____ by him, he decided city cycling wasn't for him.

4. Stephanie had an <u>itinerary</u> of all the places to visit in Spain, but she lost her travel _____ somewhere along the way.

5. When Alejandro heard the glass inside the box <u>break</u> and _____, he knew his mom's present would have to be replaced.

6. Before he <u>departs</u> for work, Mitchell turns off all the lights in his home and then he _____.

7. Katrina knew the stone was <u>artificial</u>, but she thought the _____ diamond looked very real.

8. Despite looking confident, inside Raja was <u>anxious</u> and _____.

At Home: Together, work to write sentences containing context clues that are synonyms.

Seeing Things His Own Way
Grade 6/Unit 4   117

© Macmillan/McGraw-Hill

Name _____

The suffix **-ion** means an action or a condition. When you add
it to the end of a verb, it changes the verb to a noun, as in *act +
ion = action.* Sometimes you drop an *e* from the end of the base
word when you add the ending, as in *create + ion = creation.*
Sometimes you have to change the spelling at the end of the base
word to make the new word easier to say.

Examples:

The last letters *d* or *de* become an *s.*   *explode + ion = explosion*
The last letter *t* becomes *ss.*   *permit + ion = permission*
The last letters *eive* become *ept.*   *receive + ion = reception*

**A. Add the *-ion* suffix to each of the words. Make the spelling
changes you need.**

1. extend _____

2. implode _____

3. perceive _____

4. pretend _____

5. transmit _____

6. corrode _____

7. divide _____

8. emit _____

9. deceive _____

10. transmit _____

**B. Choose two of the words you made and use them each in a sentence
of your own. Underline the *-ion* words you use.**

11. _____

12. _____

© Macmillan/McGraw-Hill

At Home: Together, see how many words you can list that
have *-ion* at the end.

Name _____

A. Write the vocabulary word that completes each sentence.

formations	wreckage	intact	severed
interior	hovering	edgy	clockwise

1. Oceanographers study the _____ of ships that have been underwater for many years.

2. Coral _____ often make up reefs where underwater life is abundant.

3. Finding an _____ ship or airplane is rare because most have sunk to the ocean floor.

4. Fish and divers alike are _____ above the ocean floor in the water.

5. Seeing the _____, or inside, of the *Titanic* is amazing!

B. Write sentences using these vocabulary words: *edgy, clockwise, severed.* Write about an experience with the ocean or with creatures that live in water.

6. _____

_____

7. _____

_____

8. _____

_____

© Macmillan/McGraw-Hill

Name _____

Read the passage. Then record three facts and three opinions presented in it.

Oceanography is the most interesting branch of science. Oceanographers go whale watching and even swim with sharks. Doing that must be really scary. They study all the animals in the ocean. Oceanographers also scuba dive. They learn to use computers that tell them about water. They even study weather. I think that being an oceanographer would be the best job in the world!

Facts:

- _____

- _____

- _____

Opinions:

- _____

- _____

- _____

What is, in your opinion, the best job in the world? Write a paragraph that contains facts and opinions to answer the question.

_____

_____

_____

_____

_____

_____

© Macmillan/McGraw-Hill

At Home: Work together to identify facts and opinions in a scientific magazine or television program.

As you read *Exploring the Titanic*, fill in the Fact and Opinion Chart.

Fact	Opinion

How does the information you wrote in this Fact and Opinion Chart help you monitor comprehension of *Exploring the Titanic*?

At Home: Have the student use the chart to retell the story.

Exploring the Titanic
Grade 6/Unit 4

121

© Macmillan/McGraw-Hill

As I read, I will pay attention to punctuation.

	Jacques Cousteau did not begin his life near the sea. He was
12	born in 1910 in France. His hometown of St.-André-de-Cubzac
20	[sant on-DRAY duh koob-ZOK] is set along a river.
25	Jacques was often sick as a boy so he did not spend as
38	much time outside as his adventurous spirit would have liked.
48	Most of his adventures came from his reading. Jacques loved
58	books about pirates, pearl divers, and distant seas.
66	Jacques had another habit during childhood. He loved
74	inventions and toying with all kinds of machinery. He saved
84	his allowance to buy one of the first movie cameras sold in
96	France. He taught himself to take it apart and put it back
108	together. When he was 13, he used the camera to shoot his
119	first film.
121	When he was a young man, Cousteau joined the navy.
131	As he traveled around the world, he became more and more
142	interested in the sea. One bright weekend morning in 1936,
151	the young sailor waded into the waters of the Mediterranean
161	Sea. 162

Comprehension Check

1. What may have influenced Jacques's decision to join the navy? **Draw Conclusions**

2. How do you know that Jacques was good at understanding machinery? **Draw Conclusions**

	Words Read	–	Number of Errors	=	Words Correct Score
First Read		–		=	
Second Read		–		=	

© Macmillan/McGraw-Hill

At Home: Help the student read the passage, paying attention to the goal at the top of the page.

Name _____

Practice

Literary Elements:
Hyperbole and
Dialogue

A tall tale features a larger-than-life hero who solves a problem in a funny or outrageous way. It includes exaggerated details.

Hyperbole is the use of exaggeration for emphasis.

Dialogue is a conversation between two or more characters. It is usually set off by quotation marks.

Common American heroes of tall tales include Johnny Appleseed, Paul Bunyan and Babe the Blue Ox, Pecos Bill and Widow Maker, and Slue-Foot Sue. All of their tales include elements of exaggeration, or hyperbole. For example, Pecos Bill was raised by coyotes, so he had a special relationship with wild animals. He first chose to ride a lion instead of a horse. When he decided on a horse to ride, he chose one that no one else would dare go near because it was so wild. Paul Bunyan was an enormous man who, with the help of his blue ox, felled many trees. He was a woodsman.

Choose one of these American heroes of tall tales and write a tall tale yourself. Be sure to include dialogue and hyperbole.

_____

_____

_____

_____

_____

_____

_____

_____

_____

_____

© Macmillan/McGraw-Hill

At Home: Discuss why the hyperbole in a tall tale makes it entertaining.

Exploring the Titanic
Grade 6/Unit 4

123

Words consist of a variety of parts: prefixes, base words, suffixes, and inflectional endings. **Suffixes** are the parts that are added at the end of words. Suffixes change the meanings and the functions of words.

Example: When I went deep-sea diving, I saw the *wreckage* of a sunken ship.

The suffix –*age* is added to the base word *wreck*. The suffix means "state of being," so the word means "something that has been wrecked." You can use your knowledge of suffixes to determine word meanings.

Write the new word formed by adding the suffixes below to the base word. Then write what the new word means.

1. active + ity = _____

2. swim + er = _____

3. place + ment = _____

4. trace + able = _____

5. hope + ful = _____

6. captive + ity = _____

7. drive + er = _____

8. state + ment = _____

9. afford + able = _____

10. cheer + ful = _____

At Home: Together, write a list of base words to which you add suffixes. Write the meanings of the new words.

© Macmillan/McGraw-Hill

Name _____

> You add the suffix **-ive** to a verb to change it to an adjective. It shows a state of being. The vowel in the suffix is short.
>
> Example: *attract + ive = attractive*
>
> You add the suffix **-age** to a verb to change it to a noun. It shows an action, a state, a number, or the cost of something. Sometimes you drop the last *e*. The vowel in this suffix is short.
>
> Examples: *post + age = postage*
>   *store + age = storage*
>
> You add the suffix **-ize** to a noun to make it a verb.
>
> Example: *civil + ize = civilize*
>
> The vowel in this suffix follows the VCe pattern. It has a long *i* sound.

Read the sentences. Underline the words that follow the patterns described above.

1. When I went scuba diving, I saw the wreckage of a ship.

2. The guide on the whale-watching tour told us about the whale's parentage.

3. The beauty of the water made its strength seem deceptive.

4. The teacher asked us to verbalize the answers to his questions as he tape recorded us.

5. We hope to formalize the agreement between the school and the state.

6. The work we have done is impressive.

Use some of the words above or others that have suffixes to make up sentences of your own. Underline the word with the suffix.

7. _____

   _____

8. _____

   _____

© Macmillan/McGraw-Hill

At Home: As a team think of as many other words that follow the patterns on this page as you can. List them.

Name _____

Write the vocabulary word that best completes each sentence.

| bewildering | moderate | hamper | prohibit | accessible |

1. Many people make medium or _____ donations to their favorite charities every year.

2. Some people find it _____ when they are faced with complicated and confusing instructions.

3. Making aid _____ to those who need it is often the job of relief organizations.

4. By giving her time, Cynthia hopes to help, not _____, the patients' progress.

5. Some organizations may _____ young people from volunteering, but others are happy to have young volunteers.

Write sentences using each one of the vocabulary words.

6. _____
   _____

7. _____
   _____

8. _____
   _____

9. _____
   _____

10. _____
    _____

© Macmillan/McGraw-Hill

Name _____

Read the passage and answer the questions.

Helping others is easy to do. From opening a door for a stranger to volunteering at a local hospital, there are many ways to help others. When you are deciding how you want to help, it is important to find the volunteer work that is right for you. If you like working with people, you might volunteer at the hospital or at a nursing home. Usually these volunteer positions allow you time to visit with people, bring them flowers, tell them stories, and just provide company. If you like working with animals, you might volunteer at an animal shelter. There you might walk dogs, clean cages, or help with adoptions. Most of your time will be spent with animals, not humans. If you like working outdoors, you might volunteer with the park service. There you might plant flowers, rake leaves, or clean up litter. However you decide to help, your time will be well spent.

1. How are the three different volunteer positions alike?

_____

_____

2. What is the difference between volunteering at an animal shelter and

volunteering at a hospital? _____

_____

_____

3. How is volunteering with the park service different from volunteering at the

hospital? _____

_____

_____

4. How is volunteering for the animal shelter different from volunteering for the
park service?

_____

_____

© Macmillan/McGraw-Hill

At Home: Plan ways to help the community or discuss ways
you already do.

Name _____

As you read *Saving Grace,* fill in the Venn Diagram.

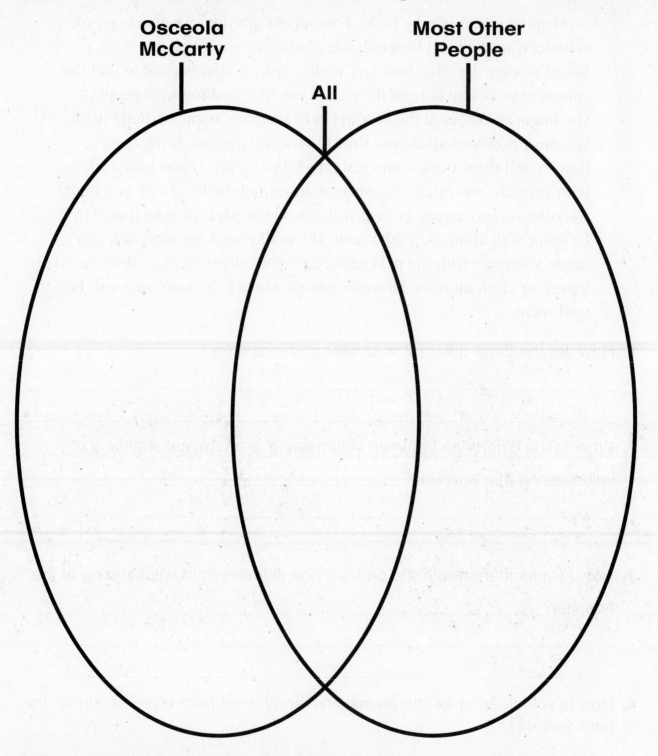

Osceola
McCarty

All

Most Other
People

How does the information you wrote in this Venn Diagram help you
monitor comprehension of *Saving Grace*?

© Macmillan/McGraw-Hill

At Home: Have the student use the chart to retell the story.

Name _____

As I read, I will pay attention to tempo or expression.

	Mary was the fifteenth of seventeen McLeod children.
8	She was one of the few born into freedom. Young Mary
19	worked the cotton and corn fields. She learned the value of
30	hard work, yet she was unsatisfied. She saw the opportunities
40	that the white children had. They went to school while she
51	worked. Mary ached for a better life.
58	Mary's mother worked for a white family. One day,
67	Mary went into the playhouse where the children did their
77	schoolwork. When Mary began to look at a book, one of
88	the girls took it away from her. She said that Mary couldn't
100	read, so she couldn't have that book. Instead she handed
110	Mary a picture book. With a heavy heart, Mary looked at the
122	pictures. After a while, her hurt hardened into a fierce
132	resolve. She *would* learn to read. No one could stop her.
143	After the Civil War, there were still two worlds in the
154	South. Education was not accessible to everyone. Many
162	whites did not think that blacks needed to read or write. But
174	Mary knew that she must learn to read to get a better life. 187

Comprehension Check

1. How was Mary McLeod's life different compared to the white children?
Compare and Contrast

2. What does Mary think she must do to have a better future? **Draw Conclusions**

	Words Read	–	Number of Errors	=	Words Correct Score
First Read		–		=	
Second Read		–		=	

© Macmillan/McGraw-Hill

At Home: Help the student read the passage, paying attention to the goal at the top of the page.

Name _____

> A **book** has different **parts**. These parts can be used to find information in the book.
>
> A **title page** is the first page and tells the title, the author, and the publisher.
>
> A **copyright page** tells when the book was written, who holds the copyright, and where the book was published.
>
> A **table of contents** lists the names of the units, chapters, or other sections of the book with the page numbers.
>
> A **glossary** defines difficult or specific terms used in the text.
>
> An **index** is an alphabetical list of all the topics covered in the book with all the corresponding page numbers.

Answer the questions.

1. Where would you look to find the author's name? _____

2. Where would you look to find the meaning of an unfamiliar word?

   _____

3. Where would you look for the beginning page number of Chapter 5?

   _____

4. Where can you find out who published the book?

   _____

5. In a book about volunteering, where would you look to find information

   about a historic event? _____

6. Explain why the different parts of a book can help you write a report.

   _____

   _____

   _____

At Home: Together, become familiar with the table of contents, glossary, and index of a book.

© Macmillan/McGraw-Hill

Homographs are words that have the same spelling. However, homographs have different definitions and sometimes different pronunciations. For example, *sow* (rhymes with *go*) means to plant seeds. *Sow* (rhymes with *now*) means a female pig. Sometimes the word is stressed on different syllables. *Object* is stressed on the first syllable when it means a thing. It is stressed on the second syllable when it means to oppose something.

Definitions are provided for the homographs. Write a sentence for each definition of the word. The sentence should make the meaning clear.

1. project: something you are working on

_____

2. project: put forth or present

_____

3. dove: a kind of bird

_____

4. dove: past tense of dive

_____

5. wind: steady gusts of air

_____

6. wind: wrap around

_____

7. lead: make the way or go first

_____

8. lead: a metal

_____

At Home: Together, list three more homographs and use each in a sentence.

© Macmillan/McGraw-Hill

Name _____

> Words can include a **prefix** at the beginning, a **base word**, and a **suffix** at the end. Knowing the meanings of some common prefixes and suffixes, along with meanings of base words, can help you figure out the meaning of a new word.

Prefix	Meaning	Suffix	Meaning
un-, dis-	not	-ful	full of
out-	in a way that is greater	-ment	result of or state of
en-	put in or on or cover with	-ly	in the manner of
re-	again or back	-ness	a state or condition of

A. In the words below, circle the prefix and underline the suffix. Then write the meaning of the word on the line following it.

1. unkindness _____

2. enclose _____

3. rearrangement _____

4. unthankful _____

5. outgrow _____

6. disagreement _____

7. retirement _____

8. unhappiness _____

9. disentangle _____

10. unpleasantness _____

B. Choose two of the words above and use each in a sentence of your own.

11. _____

_____

12. _____

_____

At Home: Together, list some words with different parts. Circle prefixes, underline suffixes, and use the word in a sentence.

© Macmillan/McGraw-Hill

Name _____

A. Write each vocabulary word next to its definition.

| demonstration | prominent | luxury | adept |
| spectators | prevail | maneuvered | collective |

1. involving all members of a group _____

2. people who watch _____

3. triumph _____

4. widely known or famous _____

5. highly skilled _____

6. showing the value of a product _____

7. changed direction and position for a purpose _____

8. condition of having comfort and pleasure _____

B. Choose four of the vocabulary words and write a sentence for each.

9. _____

   _____

10. _____

   _____

11. _____

   _____

12. _____

   _____

© Macmillan/McGraw-Hill

Facts are statements that can be proven true. **Opinions** are statements than cannot be proven true.

Each statement below is either a fact or an opinion. If the statement is a fact, write fact on the line provided. If the statement is an opinion, write opinion on the line provided.

1. Bicycling is one of many forms of exercise that young people can do.

   _____

2. Mountain bikes should be used only in the mountains, not on city streets.

   _____

3. Bicycles are a form of transportation in many parts of the world.

   _____

4. Bicycles are better than cars because they produce less pollution.

   _____

5. Learning to ride a bicycle is the easiest experience you will ever have.

   _____

6. To reduce the use of fossil fuels, people could use bicycles as their main

   form of transportation. _____

7. Bicyclists must follow the law when riding on city streets.

   _____

8. Bicycles are the best way to travel. _____

9. You don't need to worry about wearing a bicycle helmet if you're not riding

   in the street. _____

10. Before you ride a bicycle you should always check to make sure the

   brakes are working properly. _____

At Home: Together, compare facts and opinions in an article about one of the student's hobbies.

© Macmillan/McGraw-Hill

Name _____

As you read *Major Taylor*, fill in the Fact and Opinion Chart.

Fact	Opinion

How does the information you wrote in this Fact and Opinion Chart help you monitor comprehension of *Major Taylor*?

At Home: Have the student use the chart to retell the story.

© Macmillan/McGraw-Hill

As I read, I will pay attention to tempo.

	Did you know that the first bicycles were for sport and pleasure?
12	Some of the earliest bikes were luxury toys for the rich. Today, people
25	ride bikes for many different reasons. Children ride bikes for fun.
36	Your mom or dad may ride to work or to the store. Some people, such
51	as bicycle messengers, even use bikes to do their job.
61	The professional cyclist made the sport of cycling popular.
70	These athletes spend their time training and competing in national
80	and international cycling events. They appear on television. They are
90	front-page news in newspapers. Some have become the new athletes
100	of the year in sports magazines.
106	But there is one professional cyclist who changed cycling history.
116	He is Lance Armstrong. He won the Tour de France six times. The Tour
130	de France is the greatest race in cycling. No one has ever won this race
145	so many times. But there's more. In the midst of his cycling career,
158	Lance had to overcome cancer. As a cancer survivor, Mr. Armstrong
169	made the greatest comeback in cycling history.
176	Most of Lance's racing bikes are sleek and incredibly lightweight.
186	This is quite a dramatic change from early bicycles. 195

Comprehension Check

1. What is the author's purpose for including Lance Armstrong in this passage? **Author's Purpose**

2. How do you think the changes from the early bicycles helped Lance Armstrong win the Tour de France six times? **Draw Conclusions**

	Words Read	–	Number of Errors	=	Words Correct Score
First Read		–		=	
Second Read		–		=	

© Macmillan/McGraw-Hill

At Home: Help the student read the passage, paying attention to the goal at the top of the page.

Poetry uses words in special ways.

Assonance is the repetition of the same middle vowel sound in two or more closely grouped words. Example: *pudgy bug*

Onomatopoeia is the use of a word to sound like or imitate what it describes. Example: *chirp, bleep, bang*

My pup and I take to the trail
Up and down the hills, we sail
On paws, on bike, together we race,
My metal gears click into place
Thump, bump my tires pound
Pant, pant, my partner's sound
Every time by just a whisker,
The dog wins, he's just faster.
Woof, woof, he barks in victory,
That's enough, I say in misery,
I'm positive I've seen him wink
I haven't got a chance, I think.

1. Which words have assonance? _____

_____

2. Which words show onomatopoeia? _____

_____

3. How does the author use humor to show how he feels about his pet?

_____

_____

4. Write two more lines for this poem that have either assonance or show

onomatopoeia. _____

_____

© Macmillan/McGraw-Hill

At Home: Discuss words that have assonance and show onomatopoeia.

Major Taylor • Grade 6/Unit 4   137

Using analogies requires you to identify the **relationships** between words. Sometimes analogies can be synonyms or antonyms. Other times, one word might be a category of another or might be something the other does. Analogies are written like this.

diners : eat :: spectators : _____

Read the analogy like this. Diners are to eat as spectators are to _____.

Your job is to fill in the blank. First you must identify the relationship between *diners* and *eat*. When you realize that *eat* is something a *diner* does, you should then think about what a *spectator* does. This will give you the answer, *watch*.

Circle the letter of the word that best completes each analogy.

1. reader : book :: rider :
   a. magazine
   b. supper
   c. bicycle
   d. art

2. biology : science :: history :
   a. America
   b. social studies
   c. English
   d. time

3. car : steering wheel :: bike :
   a. wheels
   b. gears
   c. brakes
   d. handlebars

4. automobile : motor :: novel :
   a. plot
   b. book
   c. poem
   d. author

At Home: Together, review the relationships shown in each of the analogies above and make up some more of your own.

© Macmillan/McGraw-Hill

Name _____

Sometimes the vowel sounds of base words change with the addition of suffixes. A long sound might become a short sound. For example, *wise* has a long *i* sound, but *wisdom* has a short *i* sound.

Read the words. Explain how the underlined vowel sound in the first word changes with the addition of a suffix. Underline the changed vowel in the second word.

1. pron<u>ou</u>nce   pronunciation _____

_____

_____

2. hum<u>a</u>n   humanity _____

_____

3. s<u>ou</u>th   southern _____

_____

4. adm<u>i</u>re   admiration _____

_____

5. cr<u>i</u>me   criminal _____

_____

Choose three of the words listed above and use them in sentences. Use at least one of the words in each sentence.

6. _____

_____

7. _____

_____

8. _____

_____

At Home: Help the student tell how the vowel sound changes when a suffix is added to certain words.

Major Taylor • **Grade 6/Unit 4**   139

© Macmillan/McGraw-Hill

| arid | eaves | symmetry | furrowed |
| benefit | ceramics | derision | deftly |

A. Read the following sentences. Write a vocabulary word in each blank.

1. Other artists tried to discourage him with their _____.

2. But the unknown potter would one day be famous for his beautiful _____.

3. The _____ of the old building were covered with flowering vines.

4. The potter's brow was _____ in thought as he spun the wheel.

5. The weather in the desert is very dry and _____.

6. He _____ shaped the jug as it spun on the potter's wheel.

7. The artist painted his design without the _____ of a sketch.

8. The ancient jug showed classic _____ in its balanced design.

B. Write the letter of the definition beside each vocabulary word in column 1.

9. symmetry _____   **a.** use of ridicule to show contempt

10. arid _____   **b.** articles made of clay fired at high temperature

11. benefit _____   **c.** skillfully

12. deftly _____   **d.** part of a roof that overhangs the wall

13. eaves _____   **e.** balance

14. furrowed _____   **f.** advantage

15. derision _____   **g.** dry

16. ceramics _____   **h.** wrinkled

© Macmillan/McGraw-Hill

Read the passage and answer the questions.

When I was fourteen years old, I fled my homeland with my family. We lived in Estonia, which is in eastern Europe. The Russian army was coming to take over. The Germans, who had been occupying Estonia, were fleeing. We knew we were not safe. My father was an avid photographer, and as his daughter, I have adopted his hobby. He had shelves of photo albums, and so do I. He even took pictures of our flight. As I grew older I realized that almost all Estonians are avid photographers. When I asked an older woman about it, she explained, "We document everything we can. When you come from a country that has been occupied so many times, you know that things and people can disappear without any notice." For the first time, I realized my motivation for taking so many pictures.

1. What is the author's purpose for writing this selection?

_____

_____

2. What do you know about the author?

_____

_____

3. What do you learn about Estonians?

_____

_____

4. How does the author's perspective as an Estonian refugee affect her life?

_____

_____

_____

_____

© Macmillan/McGraw-Hill

At Home: Together, read an article from a magazine or a short story and discuss the author's perspective with the student.

A Single Shard • **Grade 6/Unit 4**   141

Name _____

As you read *A Single Shard*, fill in the Author's Perspective Web.

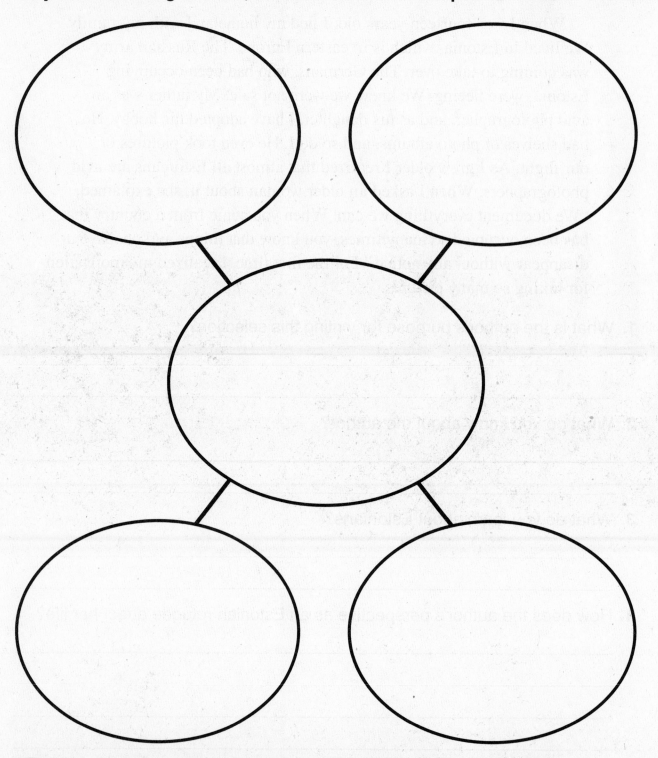

How does the information you wrote in the Author's Perspective Web
help you monitor comprehension of *A Single Shard*?

© Macmillan/McGraw-Hill

At Home: Have the student use the chart to retell the story.

Name _____

As I read, I will pay attention to pauses and intonation.

	During the Middle Ages, most people in Europe were
9	farmers. They lived in villages on the estate of a noble. They
21	grew crops and tended animals. They provided food for
30	themselves and others. They also had to make by hand
40	everything they wore or used. There were no machines.
49	At the same time, many men and women were skilled in
60	various crafts. One person in a village, for instance, might
70	be a weaver. Other villagers went to him or her for wool and
83	linen cloth to make into clothing. Villagers also needed a
93	carpenter to build their houses. They needed a blacksmith to
103	make iron tools and nails.
108	As time passed, more people needed the things made by
118	these craftspeople, such as cloth and tools. So some people
128	stopped farming and worked at their craft. People began
137	to depend on the work of skilled craftspeople. The
146	craftspeople became more specialized, and the number of
154	different crafts grew. Medieval craftspeople made everything
161	from arrows and armor to wheels and woolen cloth. 170

Comprehension Check

1. Find at least three words in the passage that are homophones. List them along with their homophones. **Homophones**

2. Why does the author write about the craftspeople? **Author's Purpose**

	Words Read	–	Number of Errors	=	Words Correct Score
First Read		–		=	
Second Read		–		=	

© Macmillan/McGraw-Hill

 At Home: Help the student read the passage, paying attention to the goal at the top of the page.

Name _____

Different **typefaces** and sizes are used to highlight important
parts of an entry in an encyclopedia.
The topic is usually bold and in a larger size than the rest of the
text.
Boldface type is used for important words. Cross-references, or
other topics that relate to the entry, are usually set in capitals.

**A. In the encyclopedia entry below, write the kind of typeface that
should be used for each term on the blank line following the term.**

Korean Pottery **1.** _____

    The Chinese influenced the style, form, glazing methods, and brush

techniques of Korean pottery **2.** _____ for
centuries. Korean merchants and traders with China probably brought back
the first examples of Chinese pottery and clay. Koreans may have even
traveled to China to learn the art of making pottery. During the

Three Kingdoms **3.** _____ period, b.c. 57

to a.d. 668 **4.** _____ Korean potters
produced plain pottery for ordinary people and very elaborate statues as
burial artifacts. The methods used to make these ceramic funeral

objects included the ancient methods of coiling **5.** _____

and hammering clay **6.** _____, and using

potter's wheels **7.** _____. Scholars have

compared the Three Kingdoms **8.** _____

pottery to the Han dynasty **9.** _____

pottery of China **10.** _____.

© Macmillan/McGraw-Hill

At Home: Make a list of topics to investigate using an
encyclopedia.

Homophones are words that are pronounced the same but have different spellings and meanings.

Example: *to, too,* and *two*

If you are confused about the meaning of a homophone, you can check a dictionary.

Read each sentence. Underline the correct homophone to complete the sentence.

1. I plan (to, too, two) attend the Native American History Conference next week.

2. I (sea, see) that they have guest speakers from several groups.

3. I want to (hear, here) about the Trail of Tears.

4. (Their, There, They're) going to have a whole day dedicated to that historical event.

5. I hope you will (be, bee) (their, there, they're) (for, four) it.

6. I like to (pier, peer) under the (pier, peer) for clams.

Use another form for the homophones from the sentences above in a sentence of your own.

7. _____

_____

8. _____

_____

9. _____

_____

10. _____

_____

At Home: Together, work to come up with a list of five more homophones.

A Single Shard • **Grade 6/Unit 4**   145

© Macmillan/McGraw-Hill

Sometimes the end consonant sound of a base word changes
with the addition of suffixes.

a. Words that end with a hard *c* often change to the soft *c* sound
with the addition of particular suffixes. For example, the hard *c*
of *physic* turns to a soft *c* in *physician*. However, it stays hard in
physical.

b. Words that end in a soft *c* often change to make the /sh/ sound
with the addition of the *–ial* suffix. For example, the soft *c* in
office changes to /sh/ in *official.*

c. Words that end in *-ct* change the /t/ sound to /sh/ with the
addition of the *–ion* suffix. For example, the /t/ in *select*
changes to /sh/ in *selection.*

**Read each sentence and underline the word that has a consonant
alternation with the addition of a suffix. Write the base word.
Then, write a, b or c depending on which of the above rules the
word follows.**

1. The facial carvings of the masks are amazing. _____

2. I feel a strong attraction to the history of art. _____

3. The columnist criticized the exhibit at the museum. _____

4. The construction of the exhibit took weeks to finish. _____

5. I am interested in the medicine men of South American Indians.

_____

**Choose three of the underlined words from the five sentences above.
Write one sentence of your own for each of the words you chose.**

6. _____

7. _____

8. _____

© Macmillan/McGraw-Hill

At Home: Together, make up a list of words that have a
consonant alteration with the addition of a suffix.

A. Fill in the blanks with vocabulary words to complete the paragraph.

guidance	typical	bewildering
benefit	deftly	derision

Every small town has a story to tell. Some stories are _____,

and others are so unusual they are downright _____. In

the Traveler's Trails, the author gives readers _____ about

these small towns. He _____ describes his journey through

the heartland without a trace of _____ for any of the

communities. In fact, he reflects on the _____ he gets from

meeting these people and learning their histories.

B. Select the vocabulary word from the box that best completes each sentence.

awesome	clockwise	luxury	ceramics

1. We fired _____ in a kiln.

2. The view from the mountain top was _____.

3. We jogged around the track in a _____ direction.

4. The palace showed evidence of great _____.

© Macmillan/McGraw-Hill

Name _____

A. Write each vocabulary word next to its synonym.

| summit | deteriorated | interior | prohibit | arid |

1. dry _____

2. inside _____

3. ban _____

4. peak _____

5. ruined _____

B. Use each of the vocabulary words listed below in a sentence of your own.

| wreckage | intact | severed | moderate | maneuvered |

6. _____
   _____

7. _____
   _____

8. _____
   _____

9. _____
   _____

10. _____
    _____

© Macmillan/McGraw-Hill

Name _____

reputation	uttered	migrant	illegally
ruptured	mistreated	wrath	quickened

A. Write the vocabulary word that matches each clue.

1. If something is spoken, it is this. _____

2. If you treated someone badly, you have done this to them.

   _____

3. This is a synonym for *anger*. _____

4. This is an antonym for *slowed*. _____

5. This means the same thing as *burst*. _____

6. If something is done unlawfully, it is done this way. _____

7. A person who moves from place to place is called this.

   _____

8. Your actions affect this, the way people see you. _____

B. Write sentences using four of the vocabulary words from above.

9. _____

   _____

10. _____

   _____

11. _____

   _____

12. _____

   _____

© Macmillan/McGraw-Hill

Name _____

A. Read each scenario. Then identify the author's purpose for writing it: *to inform, to entertain,* or *to persuade.*

1. An author writes a personal memoir about an experience with a mentor.

   Author's Purpose: _____

2. A journalist writes about a mentoring program at the local high school.

   Author's Purpose: _____

3. An author writes a short story about a boy and his mentor.

   Author's Purpose: _____

4. The mayor gives a speech asking people to join a new mentoring program.

   Author's Purpose: _____

5. A person writes a guidebook to train youth mentors.

   Author's Purpose: _____

B. Use the lines below to recommend an author whose work you really like to a friend. In your recommendation tell your friend what you like best about the author's writing and explain what you think the author's purpose is for writing a specific piece.

_____

_____

_____

_____

_____

_____

_____

_____

_____

_____

© Macmillan/McGraw-Hill

At Home: Together, review what an author's purpose might be for writing.

As you read *Breaking Through*, fill in the Author's Purpose Chart.

Clues	Author's Purpose

How does the information you wrote in this Author's Purpose Chart help you monitor comprehension of *Breaking Through*?

© Macmillan/McGraw-Hill

At Home: Have the student use the chart to retell the story.

Breaking Through • **Grade 6/Unit 5**   151

Name _____

As I read, I will pay attention to pauses, stops, and intonation.

	Mica's first day in the new house was terrible. She hated
11	it. She wanted to go back and be with Mariana. The only
23	good thing about the new house was that she didn't have to
35	share a room with Maggie anymore. Maggie was only
44	six years old, but she thought she was Mica's age. She would
56	do everything Mica did. She would borrow Mica's clothes
65	and belongings without permission. But not anymore: Mica
73	could just lock Maggie out anytime she wanted.
81	During that first week, neighbor after neighbor came over
90	to welcome the Flores family to the neighborhood. There
99	were lots of neighbors, but Mica didn't see anyone her age.
110	This made her even more depressed. She began to wonder
120	what her new school would be like. She would find out the
132	next day.
134	Mica didn't want to get up the next morning. She was
145	excited about her first day of middle school, but she didn't
156	know what to expect. Then Mica slowly rolled out of bed
167	after her mother had yelled for the fifth time for her to get up.
181	Mica locked her door and started to get ready. 190

Comprehension Check

1. How does the author make the reader feel sympathy for Mica? **Author's Perspective**

2. What do you think will happen to Mica when she goes to school? **Make Predictions**

	Words Read	–	Number of Errors	=	Words Correct Score
First Read		–		=	
Second Read		–		=	

© Macmillan/McGraw-Hill

At Home: Help the student read the passage, paying attention to the goal at the top of the page.

Name _____

A **schedule** lists times, places, or events in a table. The schedule below shows the day, times, and destinations for a cruise ship, the *Norwegian Sky,* from New England to Canada.

Schedule for the *Norwegian Sky*

Day	Port of Call	Arrival	Departure
1	Boston, Massachusetts	-----	6:00 P.M.
2	Sydney, Nova Scotia	8:00 A.M.	2:00 P.M.
3	Corner Brook, Newfoundland	8:00 A.M.	5:00 P.M.
4	Quebec City, Quebec	8:00 A.M.	-----
5	Quebec City, Quebec	-----	12:30 A.M.
6	Halifax, Nova Scotia	8:00 A.M.	8:00 P.M.
7	Bar Harbor, Maine	6:00 A.M.	5:00 P.M.
8	Boston, Massachusetts	9:00 P.M.	-----

Use the schedule to answer the questions.

1. How many days does the schedule show? _____

2. On what day and at what time does the ship arrive in Halifax, Nova Scotia?

   _____

3. On what day and at what time does the ship depart Quebec City?

   _____

4. Where will the ship be on Day 7? _____

5. In which place will the ship stay the longest?

   _____

6. In which city (other than Boston) is the stay the shortest?

   _____

© Macmillan/McGraw-Hill

At Home: Plan a trip using the above schedule.

Name _____

Meanings of words are often based on roots and base words. Words that are related are called **word families**. You can build a word family by thinking of all the parts of speech a word can be.

Word family for *illegally:* legally, legal, legality, illegal, legalize, legalization

A. Build a word family for each of the words listed. List as many related words as possible. List at least three for each word. Use a dictionary if necessary.

1. migrant: _____

_____

2. mistreated: _____

_____

3. quickened: _____

_____

4. mentor: _____

5. uttered: _____

B. Write sentences using five of the word family words that you listed above.

6. _____

_____

7. _____

_____

8. _____

9. _____

10. _____

_____

At Home: Together, work to build word families for three more words of your choosing.

© Macmillan/McGraw-Hill

Practice

Name _____

Phonics:
Homophones

> **Homophones** are words that sound alike but are spelled differently. These words are examples of the fact that different letters and combinations of letters can stand for the same sound.
>
> For example, the homophone of principal is spelled *principle*. Both the *-al* and the *-le* make the /əl/ sound.

A. Use each pair of clues to find the homophones. Make sure you spell the different words correctly.

1. two plus two / a preposition indicating purpose _____

2. a spoken or written story / a cat has one _____

3. the selling of something at a low price / a piece of cloth that helps move a boat _____

4. take a survey/a long cylinder _____

5. heaviness / remain in readiness _____

6. plant / use a needle and thread _____

7. the opposite of old / had an understanding of _____

8. a soldier who wore armor / the opposite of day _____

B. Write sentences using four of the homophones from above.

9. _____

_____

10. _____

_____

11. _____

_____

12. _____

_____

© Macmillan/McGraw-Hill

At Home: Find three homophones and use them in a sentence.

Name _____

Use the vocabulary words from the box and the clues below to solve the crossword puzzle.

grimaced   participate   ordeals   anticipated
dejectedly   encounter   nourishing   victorious

Across

3. made a facial expression of disgust

6. nutritious

7. severe trials or experiences

8. with sadness

Down

1. take part

2. having won

4. a meeting between people

5. expected

© Macmillan/McGraw-Hill

Read the passage and then fill in the chart to compare and contrast dogs and cats as pets. Use information from the passage as well as your own experience as you fill in the chart.

Dogs and Cats as Pets

   Both cats and dogs make great pets. They are soft and furry and lovable. However, they have some major differences. One of the main differences between having a dog and having a cat as a pet is the amount of care each needs. Cats need to be fed daily, and they need their litter box cleaned. They also need some attention, but not a lot. They like their sleep! Dogs, on the other hand, need plenty of attention. They, like cats, need to be fed daily. In addition, they need to be walked at least three times a day. They should have at least an hour of exercise every day. Adopting any animal is a big commitment. Adopting a dog is more of a time commitment than adopting a cat.

Cats need:	Both animals are or need:	Dogs need:

At Home: Compare and contrast two decisions you have made.

Ta-Na-E-Ka • Grade 6/Unit 5   157

© Macmillan/McGraw-Hill

Name _____

As you read *Ta-Na-E-Ka*, fill in the Venn Diagram.

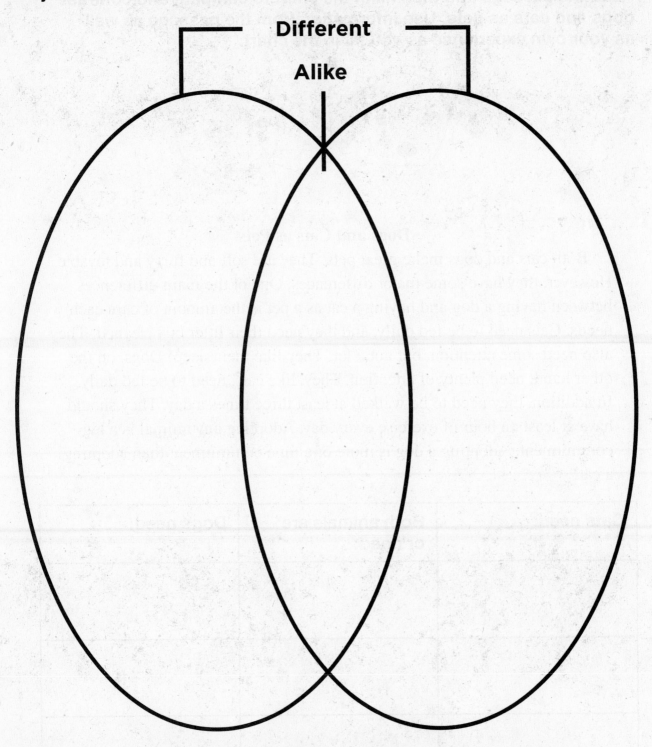

Different

Alike

How does the information you wrote in this Venn Diagram help you monitor comprehension of *Ta-Na-E-Ka*?

At Home: Have the student use the chart to retell the story.

© Macmillan/McGraw-Hill

As I read, I will pay attention to punctuation and characters' voices.

14	Most kids would fall flat on their faces if they tried to read while walking quickly, but not Stacey Taylor. She stepped nimbly over
24	sidewalk cracks, veered around a tricycle some little kid had left out,
36	and even gave her neighbor's poodle a pat on the head—all without
49	ever lifting her nose from the book in her hands.
59	The book was the true story of an amazing reporter named Nellie
71	Bly. Back in the late 1800s, most people thought that only men should
83	be reporters. But Nellie Bly did daring things that male reporters were
95	afraid to do. No adventure was too bold for her, no **ordeal** too severe.
109	She had herself locked up in an insane asylum and wrote about how
122	badly the inmates were treated. She traveled around the world by boat,
134	train, and even rickshaw.
138	Wow, thought Stacey. Wouldn't it be great to be a reporter like
150	Nellie Bly? She tried to think of something daring she could do.
162	Maybe she could discover what horrific secret ingredients were in the
173	cafeteria food.
175	Of course, for all she knew, the cafeteria served **nourishing**,
185	delicious food cooked by a gourmet chef. In fact, there were a lot of
199	things Stacey didn't know about Walker Middle School. Today was the
210	first day of the school year, and she was just starting sixth grade. 223

Comprehension Check

1. What characteristics does Stacey admire in Nellie Bly? **Make Inferences**

2. How can you tell the author admires Nellie Bly? **Author's Perspective**

	Words Read	–	Number of Errors	=	Words Correct Score
First Read		–		=	
Second Read		–		=	

At Home: Help the student read the passage, paying attention to the goal at the top of the page.

© Macmillan/McGraw-Hill

A fable is a short story that teaches a moral, often through the actions of animals that act like people.

A **moral** is a lesson taught by a fable or story. It is usually stated outright at the end of the fable.

Personification is a literary device where animals or things have human characteristics.

Read the fable and answer the questions.

The Ant and the Chrysalis

An Ant was running around in the sunshine looking for food when he came across a Chrysalis (the pupa stage of a butterfly) that was very near to changing. "Poor, pathetic animal!" cried the Ant with scorn. "What a sad fate is yours! While I can run all over the place you lie here in your shell, unable to move." The Chrysalis heard all this, but did not make any reply. A few days later, the Ant felt himself shaded and fanned by the gorgeous wings of a beautiful Butterfly. "Behold in me," said the Butterfly, "your much-pitied friend! Boast now of your powers to run and climb as long as you can get me to listen."

Moral: *"Appearances are deceptive."*

1. Who are the main characters in the story? _____

_____

2. Why does the ant think the chrysalis is pathetic? _____

_____

3. How are the ant and the butterfly like people? _____

_____

4. What is the moral of the story? _____

5. Why was the ant wrong to pity the chrysalis? _____

_____

At Home: Together, discuss how the animal characters in a fable act like humans.

© Macmillan/McGraw-Hill

Name _____

Many English words have **Latin roots**. Familiarizing yourself with Latin root meanings will help you determine the meanings of English words. These roots usually do not stand alone as words.

The Latin root *ject* means "to throw." In the word *dejectedly,* the root means "put down" or "thrown down," as in *depressed.*

A. Fill in the chart with as many words as possible that have the Latin roots as listed. Use a dictionary if needed.

1. *ject*: throw	2. *spect*: view	3. *scribe, script*: write, writing	4. *duc, duct*: lead

B. Choose six of the words you listed above and use them in sentences. Use at least one of the words in each sentence.

5. _____

6. _____

7. _____

8. _____

9. _____

10. _____

At Home: Use the word *animated* in a sentence and name the root.

© Macmillan/McGraw-Hill

Name _____

Some words in English have **Latin roots.** When you know
particular roots, you can often figure out the meaning of a word.
Roots do not normally stand on their own, so they are often in the
middle of a word, surrounded by prefixes and/or suffixes.

**Underline the Latin root of each word. Use the word in a sentence
that makes the meaning clear. Use a dictionary if you need to.**

1. project _____

_____

2. biography _____

_____

3. bookmobile _____

_____

4. microscope _____

_____

5. tractor _____

_____

6. manuscript _____

_____

7. flexible _____

_____

8. periscope _____

_____

© Macmillan/McGraw-Hill

At Home: Help the student identify the meaning of the word
spectacular.

Name _____

A. Complete each sentence with a vocabulary word.

economists   continuous   chronology   debut   periodic

1. Investors hope for a _____ and unbroken rise in the value of their investments.

2. People who are _____ study how people and governments use money.

3. There are _____ rises and declines in soccer's popularity.

4. The launch and _____ of a new sports shoe is often a publicity show.

5. The time line and _____ of the Internet is shorter than the history of the personal computer.

B. Write sentences using the vocabulary words from above.

6. _____

_____

7. _____

_____

8. _____

_____

9. _____

_____

10. _____

_____

© Macmillan/McGraw-Hill

Name _____

Sometimes writers use **persuasion** to try to make the reader think a certain way. Persuasive writing uses strong emotional words, such as *should* and *must*.

Read this passage from an editorial in a community newspaper. Then answer the questions below.

Longview Stables, founded 120 years ago, must not be closed by the city council. Although the city council wants the land for a new office building, we believe that Longview Stables should be spared. There are several reasons why. First, Longview Stables is a landmark. Second, it is the only stable in the area and provides an important service. Third, the stable also cares for horses that are ill or have been mistreated. Once the animals are well, the caretakers find new homes for them. We urge readers to write or call the mayor's office and express your support for Longview Stables. If the stable is closed, we will lose an important part of our town's heritage.

1. What opinion is expressed in the topic sentence?

_____

_____

2. What are two details that support this opinion?

_____

_____

3. What are two examples of persuasive language used in this passage?

_____

_____

4. Do you think the editorial will convince readers to oppose closing the stables?

_____

_____

At Home: Together, look at some advertisements and identify the persuasive techniques used.

© Macmillan/McGraw-Hill

Name _____

As you read *Many Countries, One Currency*, fill in the
Persuasion Chart.

Word or phrase	Kind of persuasion

How does the information you wrote in this Persuasion Chart help you
monitor comprehension of *Many Countries, One Currency*?

 At Home: Have the student use the chart to retell the story.

© Macmillan/McGraw-Hill

Name _____

As I read, I will pay attention to pronunciation of vocabulary and other difficult words.

	The Bureau of Engraving and Printing (BEP) prints all paper
10	money in the United States. The BEP was founded in 1862 during the
22	Civil War. Until that time, the federal government did not issue paper
34	money. Today it prints trillions of dollars in bills every year. Most of
47	the money that the BEP prints will replace bills that are worn or torn.
61	Paper money is very strong. But even so, dollar bills wear out in two
75	years. Other last longer, depending on their amount. The **continuous**
85	folding and handling of money wears the bills out.
94	The BEP prints bills in the following denominations: $1, $5, $10,
102	$20, $50, and $100. Bills are printed at different plants. One is in
112	Washington, D.C., and the other is in Fort Worth, Texas. Every day
124	the two plants turn out about 37 million bills with a value of almost
137	$700 million!
138	The new $20 bills contain many new security features. It has been
149	carefully designed to prevent counterfeiters from making fake money.
158	The BEP takes special care in printing bills. The bills need to last
171	as long as possible. The BEP uses special paper and inks to make
184	the bills strong. The paper and ink are also hard for outsiders to copy.
198	All through history, criminals have printed counterfeit money. 206

Comprehension Check

1. Summarize the duties of the BEP. **Summarize**

2. Why do you think paper bills feel different from regular paper? **Make Inferences**

	Words Read	−	Number of Errors	=	Words Correct Score
First Read		−		=	
Second Read		−		=	

© Macmillan/McGraw-Hill

Many Countries, One Currency
Grade 6/Unit 5

At Home: Help the student read the passage, paying attention to the goal at the top of the page.

Name _____

A **dictionary** lists definitions of words. It also provides the syllable division, the pronunciation, and the parts of speech.

mon•ey (mun ē) *n.* 1. the coins and paper currency issued by a government for payment of debt and purchase of goods and services 2. wealth in terms of funds

A **thesaurus** lists synonyms and antonyms of a word. It also lists the different parts of speech.

Example: answer
NOUNS
1. response   reply, acknowledgment, return, rejoinder
2. solution   explanation, interpretation, resolution, clue, key

VERBS
respond   reply, say, retort, echo, mimic, repeat

ANTONYMS   demand, inquiry

Use the sample entries to answer the questions.

1. What part of speech is the word *money*? _____

2. What are the two parts of speech for *answer*?

_____

3. Name a synonym for the word *answer* as a verb. _____

4. In the phrase "finding an answer," which synonym best replaces *answer*?

_____

5. In the phrase "I'm losing money," which definition best describes how *money* is used? _____

At Home: Use a synonym and an antonym for the word *answer* in two different sentences.

© Macmillan/McGraw-Hill

Name _____

Many words in English have **Greek roots**. If you know the meanings of particular roots, you can usually determine the meanings of English words.

Root	Meaning	Example
auto	self	autobiography
bio	life	biology
meter	measure	thermometer
derm	skin	dermatologist
tele	distance	telephone

Use the definitions of the roots above to help you identify the meanings of each of the following words. Write their meanings on the lines.

1. automobile: _____

2. speedometer: _____

3. biologist: _____

4. automatic: _____

5. televise: _____

6. dermatitis: _____

Choose two of the words listed above and use them in sentences.

7. _____

8. _____

_____

At Home: Together, build word families for one or two of the Greek roots.

© Macmillan/McGraw-Hill

Name _____

Some words in the English language have **Greek roots.** When you know the meaning of the Greek roots, you can figure out meanings of new words. Roots do not normally stand on their own. They can be in the middle of a word or surrounded by prefixes and/or suffixes. Sometimes the prefixes and the suffixes are also from Greek roots.

A. Underline the Greek root or roots of each word. Then write the meaning of the word on the line following it. Use a dictionary to help.

1. autograph _____

2. chronological _____

3. astronomy _____

   _____

4. photography _____

   _____

5. ecological _____

   _____

6. biology _____

7. automobile _____

8. telegraph _____

   _____

© Macmillan/McGraw-Hill

At Home: Together, think of other words that have the same roots as the word *chronological*.

Name _____

A. Match each vocabulary word to its synonym.

dilapidated   · decades   rafters   instinctively
swiveled   auction   decrease   shakily

1. trembling _____

2. decayed _____

3. lower _____

4. naturally _____

5. turned _____

6. tens _____

7. sale _____

8. beams _____

B. Write sentences using four of the vocabulary words.

9. _____

_____

10. _____

_____

11. _____

_____

12. _____

_____

© Macmillan/McGraw-Hill

Name _____

**Read the paragraphs below. Describe both sides of each argument.
Then give an explanation for your judgment.**

In the nineteenth century, many museums increased the sizes of their collections. They bought valuable objects for very low prices and carried them far from their places of origin. The British Museum bought works of art in Greece and Egypt and brought them back to London. Museums in the United States acquired many Native American objects. Some people say that these objects should be returned to their original owners. Others say that these objects should remain in museums for people everywhere to enjoy.

1. First argument: _____

_____

2. Second argument: _____

_____

3. Your judgment: _____

_____

Some people want to stop companies that make certain products from advertising. They believe that advertising some products, such as chewing tobacco, encourages young ball players to begin bad habits. Other people deny that advertising has much influence. Some also believe that companies should have the right to advertise. They believe that advertising is a form of free speech and free speech should be protected.

4. First argument: _____

_____

5. Second argument: _____

_____

6. Your judgment: _____

_____

© Macmillan/McGraw-Hill

At Home: Make an argument and then a judgment about whether cities should pass curfew laws.

Name _____

As you read *Honus and Me*, fill in the Make Judgments Chart.

Action	Judgment

How does the information you wrote in this Make Judgments Chart help you monitor comprehension of *Honus and Me*?

At Home: Have the student use the chart to retell the story.

© Macmillan/McGraw-Hill

As I read, I will pay attention to tempo.

12	"Whoever wants to know the heart and mind of America had better learn baseball."
14	A famous historian wrote those words in the 1950s when baseball had
25	been America's favorite sport for almost 100 years. People played it in
36	small towns all across the country. In the 1870s many people lived in small
49	towns. Most worked on farms. Baseball was the perfect pastime for them.
61	Baseball was a rural game. It slowly became a favorite American sport.
73	People loved baseball for many reasons. Until the last thirty or forty
85	years, mostly boys played sports. And most American boys grew up
96	playing baseball. They played it all summer long. They played in
107	schoolyards, on farm fields, and in parks. Wherever you could put out
119	four bases, you were likely to find kids playing baseball.
129	The first professional game of paid players took place in 1869 in
140	Cincinnati, Ohio. In 1876 the National League was formed. At the time
151	no other organized sports were played. Professional baseball just made
161	sense to people. It had clear rules. And people enjoyed different things
173	in the game. Some loved memorizing the statistics of individual
183	players. Others admired favorite pitchers or hitters. Still others cheered
193	for their hometown teams. For many years, baseball was the most
204	popular sport in America. It was called America's pastime. 213

Comprehension Check

1. What is the author's purpose for writing this passage? **Author's Purpose**

2. Why would someone make a judgment about Americans based on baseball? **Make Judgments**

	Words Read	−	Number of Errors	=	Words Correct Score
First Read		−		=	
Second Read		−		=	

At Home: Help the student read the passage, paying attention to the goal at the top of the page.

© Macmillan/McGraw-Hill

Name _____

Articles in magazines, newspapers, and textbooks are often accompanied by illustrations. **Photos** and illustrations enrich an article by showing the reader something words cannot. Often an illustration is accompanied by a **caption,** a sentence or two that describe what is in the picture. They give the reader additional information.

Study the illustration and caption below. Use them to answer the questions.

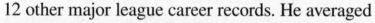

Milwaukee, 1957, National League President Warren Giles presents Hank Aaron with the 1957 National League Most Valuable Player Award.

Henry "Hank" Aaron hit 755 home runs over his career. Not only did he break Babe Ruth's record for home runs—he also established 12 other major league career records. He averaged 33 home runs a year. He drove in more than 100 runs 15 times, including a record 13 seasons in a row.

1. Who is shown in the illustration? _____

2. What made Hank Aaron famous? _____

_____

3. How many home runs did Hank Aaron hit in his career? _____

_____

4. Where and when was the picture taken? _____

5. What award did Hank Aaron receive in 1957? _____

_____

© Macmillan/McGraw-Hill

At Home: Look at some newspaper or magazine photographs with captions and discuss them.

Practice

Vocabulary Strategy:
Antonyms

Name _____

A thesaurus lists a word's **antonyms**. Antonyms are words with opposite or nearly opposite meanings. In a thesaurus, the antonym is often the last part of the entry. It is usually marked **ant.**

Example: *decrease:* lower, reduce, subtract; **ant.** increase

The antonym, or the word with the opposite meaning, of *decrease* is *increase*.

Write the antonyms of the following words. Use a thesaurus if you need to.

1. movement: _____   5. expensive: _____

2. problem: _____   6. depart: _____

3. collect: _____   7. shaky: _____

4. many: _____   8. decayed: _____

Choose four of the words listed above and use them in sentences.

9. _____

_____

10. _____

_____

11. _____

_____

12. _____

_____

© Macmillan/McGraw-Hill

At Home: Together, work on a list of words and find antonyms for them.

Name _____

The suffixes **-able** and **-ible** both mean "able or likely." You decide which spelling you will use based on whether you are attaching the suffix to a base word, such as *remark* (remark**able**) or a word root, such as *poss* (poss**ible**).

You will have to decide whether to drop the silent *e* at the end of a word when you add *-able*. Look at these two examples: manageable and excusable. When the base word ends in a soft /g/ or /c/ sound, you keep the silent *e* when you add *-able*.

Read the word parts below. Add the correct suffix, either *-able* or *-ible*. Then use each word in a sentence of your own.

1. imposs _____ _____

_____

2. reverse _____ _____

_____

3. love _____ _____

_____

4. aud _____ _____

_____

5. compat _____ _____

_____

6. horr _____ _____

_____

7. compare _____ _____

_____

8. read _____ _____

_____

At Home: Together, find more words with these suffixes and make a list of them.

© Macmillan/McGraw-Hill

Name _____

Match each vocabulary word to its definition.

convictions	oppression	evident	remedies
persistent	defiance	momentum	resonated

1. _____ evoked a positive response, echoed

2. _____ clear in vision or understanding

3. _____ medicines, cures

4. _____ the willingness to resist or challenge

5. _____ beliefs

6. _____ an unjust use of power or authority

7. _____ the strength gained through motion

8. _____ goes on stubbornly in spite of opposition

Choose four of the vocabulary words and write a sentence for each one. Write about taking a stand on an issue.

9. _____

_____

10. _____

_____

11. _____

_____

12. _____

_____

© Macmillan/McGraw-Hill

Read the paragraph. Write a summary of it in your own words.

The American women's rights movement was led by powerful women. Elizabeth Cady Stanton, Susan B. Anthony, the Grimke sisters, and Sojourner Truth took active roles in the movement during the late 1800s and early 1900s. One of the most controversial topics at the time was suffrage, or the right to vote. Some women had conventions and others staged protests in order to stand up for their rights. In the end, all the work paid off when women gained the right to vote in 1920.

1. Summary: _____

_____

_____

_____

_____

_____

2. Choose a story you have recently read. Write a one-paragraph summary of

the story. _____

_____

_____

_____

_____

_____

At Home: Help the student summarize a newspaper or magazine article.

© Macmillan/McGraw-Hill

Name _____

As you read *Let It Shine: Rosa Parks,* fill in the Summary Chart.

Beginning	Middle	End

Summary

How does the information you wrote in this Summary Chart help you monitor comprehension of *Let It Shine: Rosa Parks*?

At Home: Have the student use the chart to retell the story.

© Macmillan/McGraw-Hill

As I read, I will pay attention to tempo.

	César Chávez was one of the great labor leaders of our
11	time. Some people are driven to improve the lives of those
22	around them. César Chávez was that kind of person.
31	When Chávez was young, he and his family were
40	migrant workers. They traveled from field to field picking
49	crops. This meant the Chávez children changed schools
57	often. It also meant that the Chávez family remained poor
67	and had no permanent home.
72	César's life was filled with hardship, yet he never gave in.
83	He spent his life fighting to improve the lives of migrant
94	workers. Because of Chávez, the lives of campesinos
102	(kam-puh-SEE-nohs), or farm workers, are much better today.
109	Césario Estrada Chávez was born on March 31, 1927,
116	near Yuma, Arizona. He was the second child of Librado
126	and Juana Chávez. César was named for his grandfather,
135	which was telling. To escape **oppression** by the harsh
144	government, his grandfather had fled Mexico in the 1880s.
152	He claimed land in Arizona and started a farm. César was
163	influenced by his grandfather's love of farming and his desire
173	for a better life. 177

Comprehension Check

1. What hardships did the Chávez family experience? **Summarize**

2. What is César Chávez famous for doing? **Main Ideas and Details**

	Words Read	–	Number of Errors	=	Words Correct Score
First Read		–		=	
Second Read		–		=	

© Macmillan/McGraw-Hill

At Home: Help the student read the passage, paying attention to the goal at the top of the page.

Name _____

Words **rhyme** when their endings sound the same or nearly the same. Rhymes mostly occur at the end of lines of poetry.

A **simile** is a comparison of two essentially unlike things using "like" or "as."

Repetition of key lines or phrases emphasizes the importance of the ideas expressed in them.

A. Answer the following questions.

1. Which pair of words rhyme? _____

   a. simile/smile   **b.** rhyme/Tim   **c.** stand/grand

B. Read the simile and then answer the next two questions.

2. The army came down the mountain like a swarm of bees.

   What two things are compared in this simile? _____

   _____

3. How are the two things alike? _____

   _____

   _____

C. Write a poem about taking a stand that includes repetition. You might also include a simile or use rhyme.

   _____

   _____

   _____

   _____

   _____

   _____

© Macmillan/McGraw-Hill

At Home: Together, discuss aspects of poetry, such as
rhyme, similes, and repetition.

Let It Shine: Rosa Parks
Grade 6/Unit 5

181

Synonyms or antonyms can be **context clues**. Sometimes definitions or examples are given. The clues can come within the same sentences or they can appear within the same paragraph.

Example: Martin Luther King's words *resonated* like booming thunder in the church hall.

Use the context clues to define each underlined word. Use a dictionary if needed.

1. Oppression comes in many forms. Slavery is probably the most unfair.

   _____

2. The man's avarice showed in every aspect of his life. All he could think about was making more money.

   _____

3. It is important to acknowledge the bounty we are working so hard to achieve, such as equal rights and an end to discrimination.

   _____

4. Metropolises, such as New York and Washington, offer public buses.

   _____

5. Calculations like addition and subtraction take practice to perfect.

   _____

6. A policeman, sensing my urgency, stopped traffic to let me cross the street quickly.

   _____

7. In the silence the man's consumption of soup seemed unnaturally loud.

   _____

8. Our class shook our heads in unison because we are all in agreement.

   _____

© Macmillan/McGraw-Hill

At Home: Help the student write three sentences that provide examples of context clues.

■ **Practice**

Phonics:
Suffixes –*ant*, –*ent*;
–*ance*, and –*ence*

Name _____

The **suffixes** -*ant*, -*ent*, -*ance*, and -*ence* are closely related except for the way they are spelled.

-*ant* and -*ent*	-*ance* and -*ence*
being or performing what the root means	the quality of having, showing, or making what the root means

There is no easy rule for choosing the correct spelling, but if you know the spelling of one form, then you know the spelling of the other form.

Example: resistant, resistance   present, presence

Read each sentence below and fill in the correct suffixes. Use a dictionary to help.

1. My teacher takes attend_____ every morning. My sister is only going to have one bridal attend_____ in her wedding.

2. A private detective must be observ_____ to do his job well. The stores will be closed tomorrow in observ_____ of the holiday.

3. What is the differ_____ between bluish green and greenish blue? How are the twins differ_____ from each other?

4. The crowd responded with great exuber_____ at the town fair. Some people were so exuber_____ in fact, that they had to be asked to be quiet for the announcements.

5. My brother is always very sure of himself so he is very confid_____. He gained a lot of confid_____ as a camp counselor last summer.

6. We walked through the fragr_____ botanical gardens. The fragr_____ of the flowers was wonderful.

At Home: Have the student think of other words with these suffixes.

Let It Shine: Rosa Parks
Grade 6/Unit 5

183

© Macmillan/McGraw-Hill

A. Match each vocabulary word to its synonym.

> quickened   uttered   encounter   chronology
> dilapidated   instinctively   decrease   convictions

1. meeting _____

2. naturally _____

3. beliefs _____

4. lower _____

5. ordered events _____

6. run down _____

7. hurried _____

8. said _____

B. Write the correct vocabulary word from the box in each sentence.

> victorious   ordeals   debut   periodic   swiveled   persistent

9. The actor's film _____ was a success.

10. The _____ appearance of the whales made the town appeal to tourists.

11. The soldiers felt that the _____ of training made them stronger.

12. The player _____ at the end of the court and made a perfect basket.

13. The team was _____ because they had practiced hard before the game.

14. His _____ effort in class meant that he was successful on the exam.

© Macmillan/McGraw-Hill

Use the vocabulary words in the box and the clues to complete
the crossword puzzle.

| participate | continuous | decades | evident | oppression |
| nourishing | anticipated | illegally | reputation | defiance |

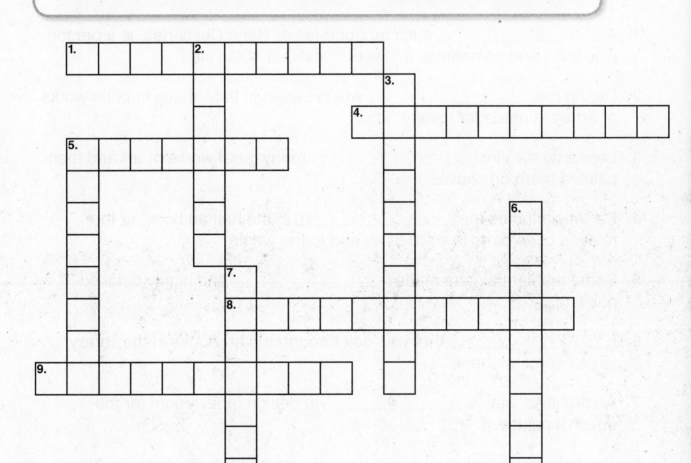

Across
1. unjust use of power
4. without stopping
5. periods of ten years
8. expected
9. character

Down
2. obvious
3. nutritious
5. willingness to resist
6. against the law
7. take part in

© Macmillan/McGraw-Hill

Name _____

Fill in each blank with a vocabulary word.

> Renaissance   philosopher   elaborate   recommend
> commissioned   miniature   envisioned   proportion

1. A _____, such as Socrates or Renè Descartes, is a person who asks and sometimes answers questions about life.

2. During the _____, which began in Italy, many famous works of art were made for royalty.

3. Leonardo da Vinci _____ many great works of art and then painted them on canvas.

4. Da Vinci studied the _____ of the human body, or the relation of its parts to each other and to the whole.

5. Some master painters made _____ and highly detailed paintings.

6. I _____ that you look through the art books in the library to see some of them.

7. An architect was _____ to design a new room for the queen's palace.

8. The king has a tiny _____ sculpture of da Vinci.

Use two of the vocabulary words in sentences of your own.

9. _____

_____

10. _____

_____

© Macmillan/McGraw-Hill

Name _____

A **generalization** is a broad statement based on a number of details. Generalizations contain words such as *all, always, often, many, most, more, less, none,* or *least.* A good generalization cannot be proved false.

Read the passage. Then read the generalizations that follow and tell whether each is valid. If a generalization is valid, underline the signal word or words in it.

Before the invention of the printing press, books were hard to obtain in Europe. Books had to be copied by hand, which took a long time and was expensive. Most books were bibles or prayer books and were owned by a church. Books were often written in Latin, even though people did not speak Latin in their daily lives. Most people were illiterate, or could not read. They did not have books to learn to read. When the printing press was invented, books became less expensive. They began to be printed in English, French, and German. Literacy rates increased.

1. Before the invention of the printing press all books were written in Latin.

   _____

2. Even though most books were printed in Latin, people did not speak Latin in their daily lives. _____

3. It was less expensive to produce all books by hand than to produce them on a printing press. _____

4. Most people were illiterate or could not read, because they did not have books. _____

5. After books were printed in English, French, and German, more people learned to read. _____

© Macmillan/McGraw-Hill

At Home: Discuss with the student the details he or she used to form generalizations.

Name _____

As you read *Leonardo's Horse*, fill in the Generalizations Chart.

Important Information	Generalization

How does the information you wrote in this Generalizations Chart help you monitor comprehension of *Leonardo's Horse*?

© Macmillan/McGraw-Hill

At Home: Have the student use the chart to retell the story.

Name _____

As I read, I will pay attention to pauses, stops, and intonation.

	Michelangelo's family had deep roots in the city of
9	Florence. His mother, Francesca, was related to a very
18	powerful man. He was Lorenzo de Medici (MED-uh-chee),
25	who ruled the city. Michelangelo's father, Lodovico
32	(loh-doh-VEE-koh), came from a long line of government
39	officials. But at the time Michelangelo was born, the family
49	wasn't doing well. Money was scarce. Yet Lodovico refused
58	to get a regular job. He thought of himself as a gentleman. In
71	those days, gentlemen didn't work, at least not with their hands.
82	The family was saved when Lodovico became mayor of a
92	small village called Caprese (kah-PRAY-zay). Lodovico and
98	his family moved into a simple stone house and began a new life.
111	Early in the morning of March 6, 1475, Francesca gave
119	birth to her second child. They named him Michelangelo.
128	When Michelangelo was still a baby, his father lost his job.
139	The family decided to return to Florence. His mother was
149	very ill at the time. She could not care for her infant son.
162	So she left him with a stonecutter and his wife. The couple
174	lived in a nearby village. Most of the men in this village were
187	also stonecutters. 189

Comprehension Check

1. Why were stonecutters not considered gentlemen? **Make Generalizations**

2. How do you know that a person's social position at this time was important? **Make Inferences**

	Words Read	−	Number of Errors	=	Words Correct Score
First Read		−		=	
Second Read		−		=	

© Macmillan/McGraw-Hill

At Home: Help the student read the passage, paying attention to the goal at the top of the page.

When you research a topic, you will often need to consult **primary sources**, such as journals and diaries, that come from the time and place you are researching.

The following excerpt is from a sailor's journal. After you read the passage, answer the questions.

September 1, 1724. Sailed day and night west, fourteen leagues. Four tropical birds came to the ship, which is a very clear sign of land, for so many birds of one sort together show that we are not lost. Twice, saw two pelicans; many weeds. The constellation called Las Gallardias, which at evening appeared in a westerly direction, was seen in the northeast the next morning, making no more progress in a night of nine hours. This was the case every night, as says the Admiral. At night the needles varied a point towards the northwest. In the morning they were true, by which it appears that the polar star moves, like the others, and the needles are always right.

1. What kind of information does the journal give?

   _____

   _____

2. Why might this primary source be useful?

   _____

   _____

3. What do you learn about life on the ship?

   _____

   _____

4. How much distance did the ship travel in the time covered in this journal entry?

   _____

At Home: Together, talk about journal writing and how it can be a helpful activity.

© Macmillan/McGraw-Hill

Words are often made up of parts, including prefixes, suffixes, and roots or base words. Knowing the meanings of **Greek roots** will help you expand your vocabulary.

A. Identify the Greek roots of each of the words. Write the root(s) and meaning on the line provided. Use a dictionary to help.

1. telegram: _____

2. cosmopolitan: _____

3. chronology: _____

4. autograph: _____

5. genre: _____

6. bibliography: _____

B. Use each of the words above in a sentence of your own.

7. _____
   _____

8. _____
   _____

9. _____
   _____

10. _____
    _____

11. _____
    _____

12. _____
    _____

© Macmillan/McGraw-Hill

At Home: Make a list of Greek roots and their meanings.

When you add the **prefixes *co, com, con, post, pro,*** or ***sub*** to words, you add a particular meaning to the word.

Here is a chart of some common prefixes and their meanings.

Prefix	co, con	post	pro	sub
Meaning of Prefix	together or with	after	in front of or for	under
Example Word	contribute	postscript	promote	subway
Meaning of Word	give, as a group	written afterward	move forward	a route under ground

If you do not know the meaning of a word and you forget what the prefix means, think of another word that has the same prefix. This can help you understand new words.

Examples: contract, convert   postmark, postseason

Underline the Greek or Latin prefix in the following words. Then write the meaning of the complete word. Use a dictionary to help.

1. co-worker _____

2. committee _____

3. proportion _____

4. cooperate _____

5. profession _____

6. submit _____

7. postpone _____

8. companion _____

9. submarine _____

10. combine _____

© Macmillan/McGraw-Hill

At Home: Work with the student to make a list of other words with these prefixes.

Name _____

Write the vocabulary word next to its definition.

immigrated	honorable	tinkering	destination
fidget	formally	glumly	unsteady

1. very unhappily or disappointedly _____

2. not firm; shaky _____

3. busy in a trifling way _____

4. worthy of respect _____

5. move in a restless way _____

6. the place to which a person is traveling _____

7. moved to live in a country where one was not born _____

8. acting with proper behavior _____

Choose six vocabulary words. Write sentences using these words.

9. _____

_____

10. _____

_____

11. _____

_____

12. _____

_____

13. _____

_____

14. _____

_____

© Macmillan/McGraw-Hill

> Events in a story happen in a certain order that is called
> **sequence**. Understanding the sequence of events can help you
> better understand what you read.

**Read the story. Then number the events to show the order in
which they occurred.**

Last night, I dreamed that I met an alien at the mall.

I went to the mall with my friend Jose who wanted to buy a new video game.
So we stopped in a video store first. Then we stopped in a shoe store that
was having a sale. Jose wanted to buy a new pair of sneakers and hiking
boots, but it was taking him a long time to make a decision. It was getting
late, so I told him I would go buy a book and come back for him.

"Your sister said to meet her at 5:30 P.M. and it's already 5 o'clock. Let's just
meet your sister in front of the ice cream store," said Jose.

"Great idea," I said. Then I headed out. I was in such a hurry that I didn't
even see that I was about to run into someone until it was too late. When
I told the "man" that I was sorry, he got very angry. That's when I saw the
third eye on his face and the extra arms on his back. I was just about to ask
what planet he was from when my alarm clock started to ring.

My alarm clock woke me up. _____

Jose and I went to the shoe store. _____

We decide to meet my sister in front of the ice cream store. _____

I left Jose to go and buy a book. _____

Jose and I went to the electronics store. _____

I went to sleep and began having a dream. _____

I went to the mall with my friend Jose. _____

I ran into an alien. _____

© Macmillan/McGraw-Hill

At Home: Together, list the sequence of events that people
might take if they were to meet an alien.

As you read *LAFFF*, fill in the Sequence Chart.

Setting

↓

Characters

↓

Events

↓

Events

↓

Events

↓

Events

How does the information you wrote in this Sequence Chart help you
monitor comprehension of *LAFFF*?

At Home: Have the student use the chart to retell the story.

LAFFF • **Grade 6/Unit 6**   195

© Macmillan/McGraw-Hill

As I read, I will pay attention to punctuation and characters' voices.

	Carter peeked over the top of the newspaper. "I'm meeting
10	some guys at the basketball courts in a little while."
20	"Isn't it kind of cold for basketball?" said Oliver.
29	"Some of us just have thick skin, I guess," Carter replied sarcastically.
41	Oliver resented how Carter acted so superior, using every available
51	chance to emphasize how he was smarter, more athletic, and more
62	adventurous than his younger brother. "Hey—I can shoot hoops. It's
73	just that Joey and I might go to the movies. . . ."
83	From somewhere, a cell phone rang. Carter rummaged around
92	for it on the table.
97	"Where did you put your phone, dear?" asked Mrs. McBride. Carter
108	knocked over an empty juice glass as he looked under napkins and plates.
121	"Ring, ring, ring," said Bailey.
126	Carter dropped to the floor. "Give me that, little missy." He snatched
138	his cell phone from Bailey's hand. Then he stood, turned, walked toward
150	the living room, and. . . .
154	Oliver replayed the next few seconds in his mind so many times, he
167	could almost convince himself it hadn't happened. "Talk to me," Carter
178	said as he answered his cell phone. As he spoke, Carter began to
191	disappear. 192

Comprehension Check

1. What events happen after the cell phone rings? **Sequence**

2. What leads you to believe the cell phone is related to Carter's disappearance? **Draw Conclusions**

	Words Read	−	Number of Errors	=	Words Correct Score
First Read		−		=	
Second Read		−		=	

© Macmillan/McGraw-Hill

At Home: Help the student read the passage, paying attention to the goal at the top of the page.

When you need to research a topic, you can use **key words** and a search engine to explore the Internet and bring up a list of Web sites. Clicking on a Web site will bring up its home page. Usually a Web site will contain other underlined words called **hyperlinks**. Clicking on a link will take you to a Web site related to your key words.

One student found this link when he looked for information on an architect whose designs interested him.

http://www.franklloydwright.com/books_about.html
Frank Lloyd Wright: The Elementary School Years by Matt Plumpton
Frank Lloyd Wright's Building Blocks by Mickey Chavez
Frank Lloyd Wright's Treehouse by Wendy Willow
Toys of Frank Lloyd Wright (1893–1909) by Megan Cho

Use the information from the Web site to answer the questions.

1. What is this Web site about? _____

_____

2. What key words might the student have used to find this Web site?

_____

3. What key words would you use to find photos of the buildings Frank Lloyd Wright designed?

_____

4. How can you order a book?

_____

5. Which link would you click on to order the book by Matt Plumpton?

_____

© Macmillan/McGraw-Hill

At Home: Together, determine what the main Web address is and what the homepage is likely to be about.

LAFFF • Grade 6/Unit 6   197

Synonyms are words that have the same or nearly the same meaning. Many words have the same denotation (literal meaning) but have different connotations (implied meanings, that suggest different things). For example, the words *cheap* and *inexpensive* are synonyms. *Cheap* has a negative connotation because it also includes the idea that the quality of an object is poor. The word *inexpensive* has a more positive connotation because it suggests that the object did not cost a lot of money. It has no reflection on the quality of the object.

Read each pair of synonyms. Write whether their connotations are positive or negative.

1. lean: _____

   scrawny: _____

2. old: _____

   senior: _____

3. fancy: _____

   gaudy: _____

4. ugly: _____

   plain: _____

5. careless: _____

   carefree: _____

6. thrifty: _____

   miserly: _____

7. picky: _____

   selective: _____

8. curious: _____

   nosy: _____

9. childish: _____

   playful: _____

10. stingy: _____

    frugal: _____

© Macmillan/McGraw-Hill

At Home: Together, discuss other words that have positive or negative connotations.

You can often recognize **absorbed prefixes**, such as *ac-*, *ar-*, *il-*, *im-*, and *ir-*, because the final consonant of the prefix is doubled. They are prefixes whose spelling changes because they would be awkward in their original form. Usually, the absorbed prefix is close to the original prefix, which you may already know.

In the words below, identify the absorbed prefix by underlining it. Then identify the original prefix from the meaning of the word.

1. immigrate _____

2. accompany _____

3. announce _____

4. arrive _____

5. illogical _____

6. irregular _____

7. illuminate _____

8. immature _____

9. arrest _____

10. illegal _____

Write sentences of your own using two of the words listed above.

11. _____

_____

12. _____

_____

© Macmillan/McGraw-Hill

At Home: Together, make a list of other words with absorbed prefixes.

Name _____

A. Fill in each blank with a vocabulary word.

anthropologists   presumably   portable   nuisance   immense

1. Communication is of _____ importance in modern daily life.

2. It is a _____ if you can't reach someone on the telephone.

3. People have been communicating _____ for thousands of years.

4. People who are _____ study the remnants of cultural communication, such as paintings and carved tablets.

5. Means of communication today, such as cell phones, are much more

   _____ than those of the past, such as stone tablets.

B. Use the vocabulary words in sentences of your own.

6. _____

   _____

7. _____

   _____

8. _____

   _____

9. _____

   _____

10. _____

    _____

© Macmillan/McGraw-Hill

Read the passage.

Many products today are advertised in terms of **problem and solution**. For example, hair conditioner is supposed to be a solution to the problem of dry, tangled, and damaged hair.

Create your own product to be used in the home. Design an advertisement that describes a problem and tells how your product will provide the solution to that problem. Draw your advertisement in the box. Then use your advertisement to answer the questions below.

1. What is the name of your product? _____

2. What problem does your product solve?

_____

_____

3. How does your product solve the problem?

_____

_____

_____

_____

© Macmillan/McGraw-Hill

At Home: Discuss with the student how an ordinary product used in your home solves a problem.

These Walls Can Talk
Grade 6/Unit 6
201

Name _____

As you read *These Walls Can Talk,* fill in the Problem and Solution Chart.

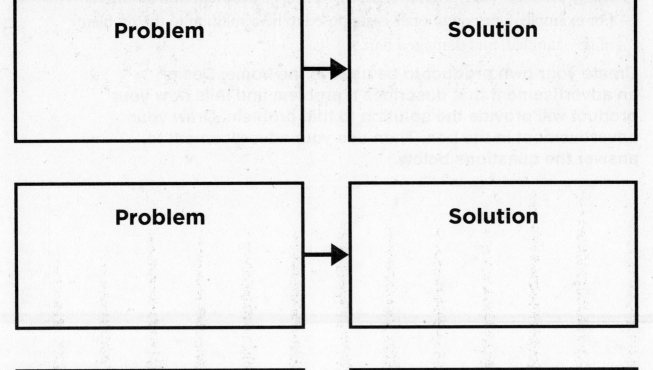

Problem		Solution

Problem		Solution

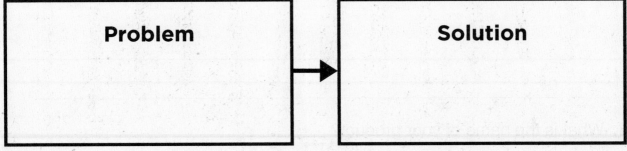

Problem		Solution

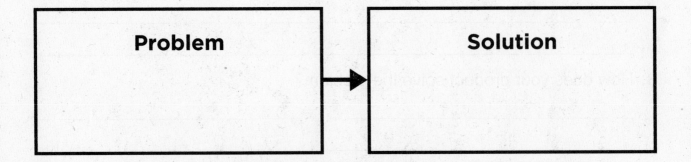

Problem		Solution

How does the information you wrote in this Problem and Solution Chart
help you monitor comprehension of *These Walls Can Talk*?

© Macmillan/McGraw-Hill

At Home: Have the student use the chart to retell the story.

As I read, I will pay attention to the pronunciation of vocabulary and other difficult words.

	In the 1900s, airplanes crossing the deserts of Peru made an
10	amazing discovery. Passengers looked out of the windows and saw
20	**immense** drawings scratched into the earth. These drawings showed
29	birds, mammals, bugs, and patterns.
34	People on the ground did not know that these drawings existed.
45	Yes, they knew that lines were scratched into the ground. They could
57	see them clearly. However, until people saw the lines from the sky, they
70	had no idea that the lines formed pictures.
78	Most people believe that the drawings were made by the Nazca
89	people. They lived in that area around 200 B.C.E. They lived in Pampa
101	Colorado, which means Red Plain. The surface there is flat and stony.
113	The surface pebbles are reddish. Only the surface is red, though, while
125	the soil below is much lighter. The lines were made by removing
137	topsoil so that the lighter soil showed through.
145	Scientists have studied these images for years. The images raise
155	many questions. How were these lines created and by whom? What
166	was the purpose of these drawings? So far, there have been no solid
179	answers. But scientists do have some theories. 186

Comprehension Check

1. How did people discover the giant drawings? What was the effect? **Cause and Effect**

2. Why is it difficult to know exactly who made the drawings? **Make Inferences**

© Macmillan/McGraw-Hill

	Words Read	–	Number of Errors	=	Words Correct Score
First Read		–		=	
Second Read		–		=	

At Home: Help the student read the passage, paying attention to the goal at the top of the page.

Name _____

> **Functional documents** give you information to help you complete tasks, decide on purchases, or get from one place to another. They might also provide information about an organization or community. It is important to be able to interpret such documents in order to access the information you need.

What if you were going to see a friend at his house? You have never been there before. He gives you these directions. Read the directions and then answer the questions.

1. Walk down Duffield Street until you run into Tillary Street.
2. Turn right on Tillary Street.
3. Make an immediately left on Flatbush Avenue.
4. Walk down Flatbush Avenue, past the gas station.
5. Turn right on Myrtle Avenue. There is a restaurant on the corner.
6. Walk down Myrtle Avenue. At the second stoplight, turn right onto Ashland Place.
7. My house is on the right, before you get to Willoughby Street.

1. What is the purpose of this functional document? _____

_____

2. What is the first turn that you would make? _____

_____

3. How many streets will you walk on to get to your friend's house? _____

4. Where is your friend's house located? _____

_____

5. What markers does your friend use to help you find the streets? _____

_____

© Macmillan/McGraw-Hill

At Home: Help the student write directions from your home to a neighborhood location.

Words can be made up of prefixes, suffixes, and roots. Roots are different from word bases because they cannot stand alone. Many words in the English language trace their history back to Greek and Latin. If you learn the meanings of several basic **Greek and Latin word roots,** you will unlock the key to a larger English vocabulary. Knowing the basic meanings will allow you to grasp the meanings of seemingly unfamiliar words.

Review the chart. Use the meanings of the word parts to help you define the words below.

Root	Meaning	Example
ject	throw	*eject*
auto	self	*automobile*
bio	life	*biology*
graph	write	*autograph*
tele	far away	*telescope*
manu	hand	*manufacture*
cent	one hundred	*centuries*
logy	science of	*zoology*

1. reject: _____

2. autograph: _____

3. manuscript: _____

4. centennial: _____

5. zoology: _____

6. telephone: _____

7. manual: _____

8. biology: _____

At Home: Challenge the student to combine the Latin and Greek word parts to make at least three words.

© Macmillan/McGraw-Hill

The **Greek suffixes** -logy or -ology mean the science or the study of whatever the root or base word indicates. *Biology* is the science of plant and animal life.

The suffix -ician means practitioner, someone who practices or works with whatever the root or base word indicates. A *musician* is someone who practices or plays music.

The suffix -crat means a person who rules or governs. An *autocrat* is someone who rules all by himself or herself.

Using what you know about Greek suffixes, write a definition of each word listed below. Then use the word in a sentence of your own.

1. politician _____

_____

2. technology _____

_____

3. aristocrat _____

_____

4. ecology _____

_____

5. electrician _____

_____

6. bureaucrat _____

_____

© Macmillan/McGraw-Hill

At Home: Together, make a list of other words with these suffixes.

Name _____

Use the vocabulary words and the clues to complete the crossword puzzle.

| guilds | established | scribes | obstacles |
| privileged | manuscripts | alloy | penniless |

Across

1. gained full acceptance

3. enjoying an advantage

5. people who write

7. written documents

Down

2. a substance composed of two or more metals

3. having no money

4. things that get in the way

6. associations or unions of craftspeople

© Macmillan/McGraw-Hill

Name _____

When you use words to describe something your mission is to create a striking image or **description** for your readers. Use vivid, specific details to tell your reader how the subject looks, sounds, smells, tastes, or feels.

Look at the list of items below. Each one appeals to the senses of sight and sound, as well as smell. Choose one item, circle it, and answer the questions that follow.

A trip to the zoo   A trip to the movies   A trip to a baseball game

1. What smells go along with this scene? _____

_____

2. What sounds do you hear? _____

_____

_____

3. What tastes go along with this scene? _____

_____

4. What might appeal to your sense of touch? _____

_____

5. Finally, what do you see? _____

_____

At Home: Ask the student to describe something in the room where you are, using words that appeal to all five senses.

© Macmillan/McGraw-Hill

Name _____

As you read *Breaking into Print,* fill in the Description Web.

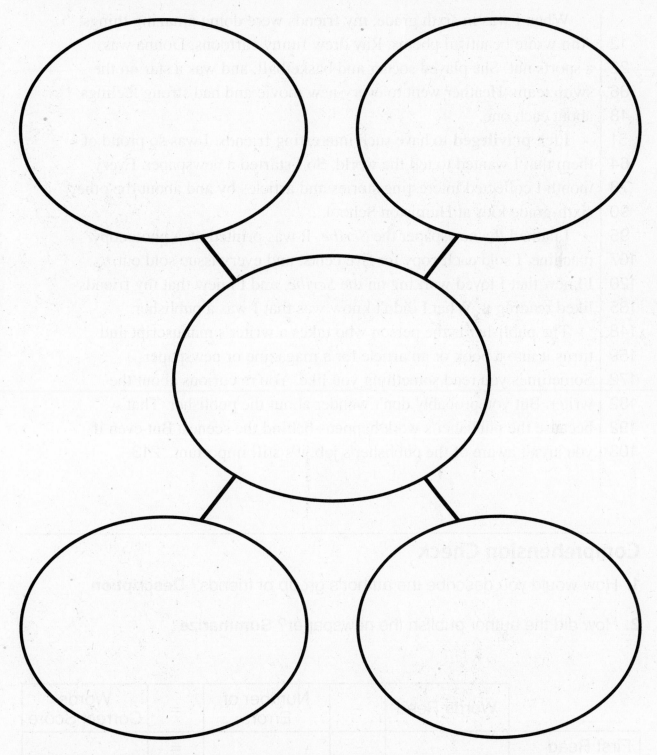

How does the information you wrote in this Description Web help you
monitor comprehension of *Breaking into Print*?

 At Home: Have the student use the chart to retell the story.

Breaking into Print
Grade 6/Unit 6

209

© Macmillan/McGraw-Hill

Name _____

As I read, I will pay attention to tempo.

	When I was in sixth grade, my friends were doing amazing things.
12	Ann wrote beautiful poems. Ray drew funny cartoons. Donna was
22	a sports nut. She played soccer and basketball, and was a star on the
36	swim team. Heather went to every new movie and had strong feelings
48	about each one.
51	I felt **privileged** to have such interesting friends. I was so proud of
64	them that I wanted to tell the world. So I started a newspaper. Every
78	month I collected interesting stories and articles by and about the other
90	sixth-grade kids at Humiston School.
95	I named the newspaper the *Scribe*. It was printed on a photocopy
107	machine. I sold each copy for five cents, and every issue sold out.
120	I knew that I loved working on the *Scribe,* and I knew that my friends
135	liked reading it. What I didn't know was that I was a publisher.
148	The publisher is the person who takes a writer's manuscript and
159	turns it into a book or an article for a magazine or newspaper.
172	Sometimes you read something you like. You're curious about the
182	writer. But you probably don't wonder about the publisher. That's
192	because the publisher's work happens behind the scenes. But even if
103	you aren't aware of the publisher's job, it's still important. 213

Comprehension Check

1. How would you describe the author's group of friends? **Description**

2. How did the author publish the newspaper? **Summarize**

	Words Read	–	Number of Errors	=	Words Correct Score
First Read		–		=	
Second Read		–		=	

© Macmillan/McGraw-Hill

At Home: Help the student read the passage, paying attention to the goal at the top of the page.

Rhyme scheme is the pattern made by the end rhymes in the lines of a poem. Schemes are marked by lowercase letters that show which lines rhyme, such as *aabb*.

Rhyme schemes create a **rhythmic pattern**, or a predictable sound, for each stanza of a poem.

Personification is a comparison in which human qualities are given to objects, ideas, or animals.

Read the poem and answer the questions.

A Poem Has Life
by Meg Mackenzie

I have so many things to say
I must be sure to sing all day.
When cause and word are in the heart,
It must give voice for that's the art.

I simply know that poems must shout,
Though words don't easily come about.
But fight the fight I must,
    or cry.
I am a poet; I know not why.

1. What is the rhyme scheme of the poem? _____

2. Which lines give examples of personification? _____

_____

_____

3. What is this poem about? _____

_____

4. How many beats are there in each line? _____

© Macmillan/McGraw-Hill

At Home: Together, write a narrative poem about a recent event.

Name _____

Many English words have **Latin roots**. Roots are different from base words. They cannot stand alone as words. Familiarizing yourself with Latin root meanings will help you determine the meanings of many English words.

The Latin root *manu* means "hand." The Latin root *script* means "text." A *manuscript* is text, or material written by hand.

A. **Use a dictionary to make eight words from the Latin roots *manu* and *script*.**

1. _____
2. _____
3. _____
4. _____
5. _____
6. _____
7. _____
8. _____

B. **Write four sentences using the words that you made from the Latin roots *manu* and *script*.**

9. _____

_____

10. _____

_____

11. _____

_____

12. _____

_____

At Home: Together, make a word family using the Latin root *ject*.

© Macmillan/McGraw-Hill

Many words in English come from Greek and Roman **mythology**. The gods and goddesses of these early myths had certain characteristics that are reflected in the modern words formed from their names. An example of a word taken from mythology is *cereal*. This word is from *Ceres*, the Roman goddess of agriculture, because *cereal* is made from grain.

Study the words in the chart that are taken from Greek or Roman mythology. Choose five of the words and use each in a sentence of your own. Underline the words in your sentences.

Word	Word from Mythology
east	Eos: Greek goddess of the dawn
flower	Flora: Roman goddess of flowers
martial	Mars: Roman god of war
panic	Pan: Greek god of sheperds
jovial	Jupiter: Most powerful Roman god
volcano	Vulcan: Roman god of fire
Saturday	Saturn: Roman god of agriculture
January	Janus: Roman god of beginnings
May	Maia: Roman goddess of growth

1. _____

2. _____

3. _____

4. _____

5. _____

_____

© Macmillan/McGraw-Hill

At Home: Together, make a list of words that come from mythology.

A. Each vocabulary word is shown in context in the sentences below. Circle the context clues as you read 1–8.

dwelling	ambitious	lounge	pondering
drowsy	revived	agonized	vapors

1. Mateo's house or <u>dwelling</u> was in the path of the volcano.

2. Caitlin was an <u>ambitious</u> girl: She wanted to be successful.

3. Carlin did not waste time and <u>lounge</u> around in an unproductive way.

4. Juanita spent her afternoon <u>pondering</u> her schedule, thinking about what to do next.

5. This medicine might make you feel <u>drowsy</u> or sleepy.

6. A good night's sleep <u>revived</u> the weary traveler and energized him.

7. Kim <u>agonized</u> and suffered over her decision.

8. She knew if the volcano erupted, the <u>vapors</u> would be gases and debris.

B. Use the context clues to write the definition of each vocabulary word on the line provided.

9. dwelling _____

10. ambitious _____

11. lounge _____

12. pondering _____

13. drowsy _____

14. revived _____

15. agonized _____

16. vapors _____

© Macmillan/McGraw-Hill

The **theme** is the main idea of a story. Authors often do not state the theme directly. They reveal it through the interaction of the characters, or in actions, or conflict. The theme can usually be summed up in one sentence. For instance, consider the story of the tortoise and the hare. In this well-known story, the tortoise and the hare are in a race. Of course, the hare can run very fast, and everyone (especially the hare) is sure that he will win the race. The tortoise cannot run at all, and walks very, very slowly. But the hare is overconfident, and he stops to rest between spurts. The tortoise continues on his way, slowly but surely, and reaches the finish line first. The theme of the story, never directly stated by the author, is, "Slow and steady wins the race."

Read the passage below. Then answer the question.

The ground was shaking from the earthquake as Melvin stood outside his apartment building at the end of the street. His mother stood next to him and silently grabbed his hand. Melvin looked at her and realized they were totally unprepared. What should they do? Where could they go? Melvin had no idea. He looked back into the apartment building and then at his mother. He realized that everything they had—all their furniture, pots and pans, and clothing—meant nothing unless he and his mother lived through this awful day. He turned back to her and said, "We can run very fast if we take nothing."

Circle the theme that best states the main idea or message of the story.

When trouble comes, people reach out to help each other.

When trouble comes, people realize what they value most in life.

When trouble comes, people show their worst traits because they are afraid.

© Macmillan/McGraw-Hill

At Home: Together, discuss what the story would be like if it had one of the other themes.

Name _____

As you read *The Dog of Pompeii,* fill in the Theme Chart.

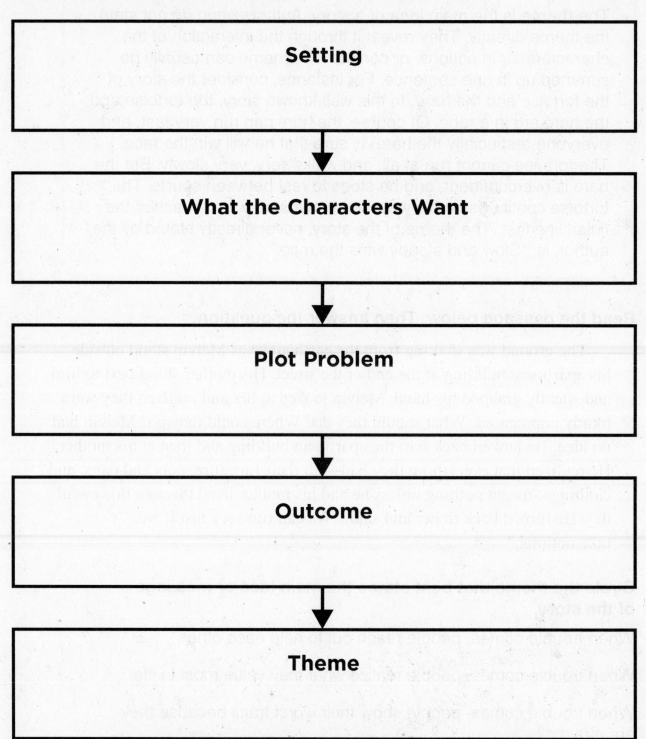

Setting

What the Characters Want

Plot Problem

Outcome

Theme

How does the information you wrote in this Theme Chart help you
monitor comprehension of *The Dog of Pompeii*?

At Home: Have the student use the chart to retell the story.

© Macmillan/McGraw-Hill

Name _____

As I read, I will pay attention to pauses and intonation.

11	"What do you figure Pa'll bring back from his trip?" Seth asked Jed.
13	"He's bound to bring back news about what's happening in
23	the rest of the world. And you know he'll have a tall tale about his
38	adventures at the trading post," answered Jed, chuckling.
46	"Do you remember the story about the time the syrup trapped
57	him?" giggled Seth.
60	"As I recollect," recounted Jed, "Pa said he'd been doing a fair
72	bit of **pondering** at the trading post, trying to decide which of the
85	fabrics Ma would like for a new dress and which ones he should
98	buy for the little ones' smocks. He was mighty tired looking at all
111	those bolts of cloth, so he leaned his elbows on the counter,
123	looking left, right, up, and down, over and over, until finally he'd
135	made his decisions. But when he tried to stand up, he couldn't
147	budge! His elbows were stuck in a pool of syrup that he hadn't
160	noticed was on the counter.
165	"And the syrup had hardened by the time Pa wanted to stand
177	up, so he felt like a beetle trapped in pitch," finished Seth, nearly
190	convulsed with laughter. "Do you remember how Pa showed us
200	what had happened to him?" 205

Comprehension Check

1. What happens while Pa is at the trading post? **Summarize**

2. Why do you think Pa tells his children tall tales? **Make Inferences**

	Words Read	−	Number of Errors	=	Words Correct Score
First Read		−		=	
Second Read		−		=	

© Macmillan/McGraw-Hill

At Home: Help the student read the passage, paying attention to the goal at the top of the page.

Name _____

> **Graphic aids** can help you understand processes and events. Graphic aids include diagrams, charts, tables, illustrations, graphs, and photographs. Graphic aids should help you better understand the text they accompany and should provide additional information.

How a Volcano Forms

When a volcano erupts, lava and other materials flow onto Earth's surface. The materials pile up around the opening as they cool. Over time a mountain may form. Both the opening and the mountain around it are called a *volcano*.

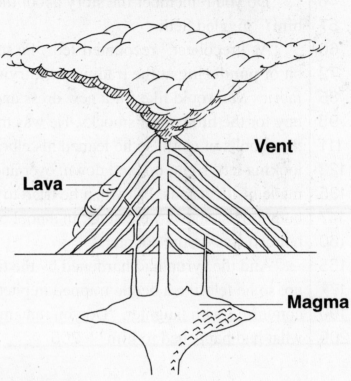

Use the diagram to answer the questions.

1. What is shown in the diagram? _____

_____

2. What is the part of the volcano through which the lava erupts? _____

_____

3. What causes the mountain part of the volcano to form? _____

_____

4. What is lava called before it erupts? _____

_____

© Macmillan/McGraw-Hill

At Home: Discuss with the student several other questions about this diagram.

Name _____

Multiple-meaning words have more than one meaning. Context will often allow you to determine which meaning of a word is being used.

Example: I went to the <u>lounge</u> to get a bottle of water.
         I <u>lounge</u> about all day on Saturdays.

In the first example, the word *lounge* refers to a "place to get refreshments." In the second sentence, *lounge* means "relax."

Each of the following words has more than one meaning. Write at least one sentence for each meaning of the word.

1. content _____

   content _____

2. frank _____

   frank _____

3. lark _____

   lark _____

4. mount _____

   mount _____

5. paddle _____

   paddle _____

6. object _____

   object _____

7. conductor _____

   conductor _____

8. fine _____

   fine _____

© Macmillan/McGraw-Hill

At Home: Ask the student to list three more multiple-meaning words and use them in sentences.

The English language borrows many words from around the world. Some of the words are cognates, or spelled and pronounced almost the same way as they are in the original language. Others are words made of foreign phrases. Knowing a word's original meaning can help you understand and remember it.

A. Use a dictionary to find the original language and meaning of each word.

1. gong _____

_____

2. algebra _____

_____

3. pizza _____

4. typhoon _____

5. bazaar _____

6. denim _____

_____

7. bronco _____

8. sombrero _____

9. caribou _____

10. igloo _____

B. Choose two of the words above and write a sentence for each one.

11. _____

_____

12. _____

_____

At Home: Together, make a list of other words that might be taken from other languages.

© Macmillan/McGraw-Hill

Name _____

A. Match each vocabulary word to its antonym.

honorable	unsteady	portable	immense
privileged	ambitious	lounge	drowsy

1. exercise _____

2. awake _____

3. needy _____

4. stable _____

5. lazy _____

6. disreputable _____

7. tiny _____

8. immoveable _____

B. Use these vocabulary words in the following sentences.

philosopher   Renaissance   elaborate   miniature   fidget   glumly

9. I could not help myself as I began to _____ in my seat when the lecture went on too long.

10. I answered the teacher's questions _____ because I wanted to be outside.

11. The model train was so beautiful with all its _____ figures and buildings.

12. During the _____, artists such as da Vinci became famous for their painting.

13. Socrates was a famous _____ in ancient Greece.

14. The frame around the picture was so _____ the picture was hard to see.

© Macmillan/McGraw-Hill

A. Fill in each blank with a vocabulary word.

recommend	envisioned	immigrated	destination	anthropologists
nuisance	pondering	established	obstacles	manuscripts

1. The artist _____ a life-size statue made of bronze.

2. Many people have _____ to the United States.

3. Genevieve was _____ her next chess move.

4. _____ face many _____ in their work.

5. Sometimes it is a _____ to travel to such

   a far-off _____.

6. The magazine will _____ the best books to read.

7. The author submitted several typed _____.

8. It is important to bank with an _____ company.

B. Use six vocabulary words to write sentences of your own.

9. _____

10. _____

11. _____

12. _____

13. _____

14. _____

© Macmillan/McGraw-Hill